I Can't Do
Why childr
say it and how to
make a difference

Professor Alf Coles and
Professor Nathalie Sinclair

BLOOMSBURY EDUCATION
LONDON OXFORD NEW YORK NEW DELHI SYDNEY

BLOOMSBURY EDUCATION
Bloomsbury Publishing Plc
50 Bedford Square, London, WC1B 3DP, UK
29 Earlsfort Terrace, Dublin 2, Ireland

BLOOMSBURY, BLOOMSBURY EDUCATION and the Diana logo are
trademarks of Bloomsbury Publishing Plc

First published in Great Britain, 2022 by Bloomsbury Publishing Plc

This edition published in Great Britain, 2022 by Bloomsbury Publishing Plc

A catalogue record for this book is available from the British Library

ISBN: PB: 978-1-4729-9267-3; eBook: 978-1-4729-9269-7;
ePDF: 978-1-4729-9270-3

2 4 6 8 10 9 7 5 3 1 (paperback)

Typeset by Newgen KnowledgeWorks Pvt. Ltd., Chennai, India
Printed and bound in the UK by CPI Group (UK) Ltd., Croydon, CR0 4YY

To find out more about our authors and books visit www.bloomsbury.com
and sign up for our newsletters

Contents

Acknowledgements

We would like to acknowledge the contributions of Sandy Bakos and Annette Rouleau, who read drafts of the book and provided excellent advice on how to make our arguments both more convincing and more accessible. Their own longstanding experiences as primary school teachers provided a precious contribution. To David Pimm, we thank you for your generous reading of the book, always attentive to potential connections and clear turns of phrase. And to Caroline Ormesher, thank you for the invaluable comments on early chapters, which helped set us on our way. We would also like to thank our editor Cathy Lear for the care taken with the full manuscript and the many suggestions to improve the flow and readability of the writing.

Introduction

'My pupils won't understand if it's not made concrete.'

We've all heard this idea before. These words are almost always said about maths. If the problem is that maths is abstract, then the solution seems obvious: we need to make it more concrete. Almost everyone agrees with this. Around the world, new approaches, new curricula, new tasks, new teaching strategies, new manipulatives and new technologies are suggested, often aiming to fix the problem in the same way – by making maths concrete.

But what if that's not the problem? What if there were other ways to explain the fact that so many people worldwide struggle to understand school maths? The premise of this book is that the chronic, long-standing failures in the maths classroom – which have significant consequences for children's wellbeing and for teachers' wellbeing as well as for the planet's wellbeing – are not the result of the maths-is-too-abstract problem. In fact, we think that although this problem and a few others have driven change in the maths education system, they all need rethinking. From our experiences working in maths education over the last 25 years, we have distilled the following five dogmas – core assumptions that are generally believed to be true about maths:

A. 'Maths is a building block subject.'

B. 'Maths is always right or wrong.'

C. 'Maths is culture-free.'

D. 'Maths is for some people, not others.'

E. 'Maths is hard because it is abstract.'

We feel sure that you've come across these ideas before, though perhaps in slightly different forms. We call them dogmas because they seem incontestable to almost everyone – obvious statements about learning maths. It's true that if they were completely wrong, they might not be quite so pervasive. But in this book, we argue that they represent beliefs, rather than facts. We show how, through history, these beliefs have evolved, and why they are so hard to even question. We offer different perspectives, different ways of thinking and of working, which show the limitations of these dogmas. We aren't proposing these are the only five dogmas, but we think they're pretty major ones.

Importantly, we're not claiming that the dogmas are all entirely wrong and that educational change can only happen if we overturn them. For at least a century, people have swung between opposing views on how to teach maths and tried to replace one system with another, usually its opposite. That is how we've had problem-solving replacing exercises, or conceptual maths replacing procedural maths, or student-centred replacing teacher-centred teaching, and back again. These are false dichotomies. All these approaches can be effective and valid in one context or another.

So even though we present other perspectives that challenge these five dogmas, we're not trying to convince you to turn your back on them completely. But we hope that you might be surprised by some of our alternative perspectives. We hope that, after reading this book, you'll recognise cases of dogmatic ways of thinking about maths teaching and learning, and be able to make a more informed choice. Most importantly, we hope that you respond differently if you find yourself or your pupils thinking 'some people can't do maths' or 'maths is the same everywhere' or 'I can't teach this person without them understanding the basics first'. We hope to show that the challenges you're facing aren't quite so obvious.

One reason these dogmas are so pervasive is that they draw on deeply ingrained ways of thinking that we use, not just when thinking about maths, but in many other contexts as well. For example, the second dogma ('Maths is always right or wrong') represents a kind of binary thinking that runs deep in Western logic and shapes how we think about many things. We associate the dogmas with visual ways in which we imagine relationships. In the case of the dogma that maths is always right or wrong, this might be the image of a balance which tips one way or the other. For example, we think of time passing between night and day. These two things – night and day – become opposites of each other, binary choices, and we come to believe that it's either night or day (*exclusively* one or the other). But if we stop a moment, we realise that over the course of a 24-hour period, there are times when it is in between night and day, like dusk or dawn. You could even see the 24-hour period as a continuum between having no light from the sun and having maximum light from it. This example might not seem very important, but we think that moving away from binary thinking can have significant effects in the maths classroom. This will become apparent in Dogma B, where we show that mathematics is not always just right or wrong. It will also be relevant to Dogma D, where we challenge the binary in which you are either good at maths or not.

For each dogma, we've provided images that represent it and possible alternatives. We start each Dogma chapter with a story that's helped our own thinking about how these dogmas function and how they might be expanded upon. Following each Dogma chapter, we discuss related classroom-based activities and case studies in a Putting into practice chapter. You could decide to read a Putting into practice chapter first, and then go back to the associated Dogma chapter for more historical context.

As society becomes ever more technological and driven by algorithms, we think that maths education is critical for helping people to be conscious of the way their societies are organised, and to be aware of the role maths plays in decision-making. For example, as change in the climate occurs at an ever-increasing pace, we see a vital role for maths education in supporting citizens to have the tools to track and communicate about those changes and model possible futures. In the UK, we can't afford to continue letting the roughly 20 per cent of each cohort of school students reach the age of 16 feeling they have failed in maths. We'll surely need everyone to play an active role as a citizen in the changing and precarious times to come.

We were both teachers, before moving to our current roles in universities. We don't lay blame for the levels of underachievement in maths at the door of teachers and schools. In our experience in England, Canada and across the world, we meet teacher after teacher who is committed and dedicated to their students and works all hours to support their learning. What we see as problematic are widespread assumptions about teaching and learning – assumptions which have become dogmas that work against the aims of schools and of teachers – which affect the expectations of policy-makers, parents and even children.

We're writing this Introduction at a moment, in England, when there is a push towards 'mastery' teaching in mathematics. This push could be seen as one of the swings mentioned above. The ambition of mastery teaching is to eradicate underachievement in maths. This is a fantastic ambition and aim. But we believe it will only succeed in the long term if it brings with it a rethinking of some of the dogmas described in this book. We'll cover ideas of mastery teaching at points throughout the book.

If you're reading this book, it is probably because you had suspicions of your own about the five dogmas. Or, you're not sure how you can help a child saying to you, 'I can't do maths!' Or, maybe you feel that way yourself. We're not offering simple solutions, because each child's reason for saying this will be different. However, we hope that the new perspectives we offer will extend your ideas, and provide stories and images which will be helpful in thinking about maths for yourself and in your conversations with others.

We're convinced that *every* child who speaks their home language has all the skills they need to be successful in primary school maths. But there's no magic bullet; we don't claim to know what every child needs or that it's easy to find out. There will be ideas in this book which can be tried out immediately, i.e. actions you can test, as well as an invitation to reflect on actions – and it's the combination of action and reflection which is needed for any lasting change.

Dogma A: 'Maths is a building block subject'

Alf's story

I taught maths in schools for 17 years. This inevitably meant that friends would sometimes approach me and ask if I could help their children with particular aspects of the subject. I was always pleased to help. One time stands out. Joe, the son of some friends, was doing a PhD. He was applying to switch to a public university in the US, which meant that he had to take the US SAT examinations. These included some maths that often appears on secondary school curricula, including some fraction calculation questions. Joe confessed to having a complete blind spot about fractions. In particular, he came to our first meeting with the question: what is $\frac{2}{1/3}$?

Joe, with some amusement at himself, spoke about not even being able to say this fraction: 'Is it two one thirds? That couldn't be it. Two of one third, that's not right either.' (There is actually no neat way of expressing the fraction in words in English; a mathematician might say: 'two over one third'.)

Some context about Joe is important here. He was doing a PhD in an economics-related subject, i.e. in a highly mathematical subject. Joe had taught master's level economics courses, including solving complex differential equations involving algebraic fractions. In other words, he had mastered some highly complex mathematics involving sophisticated uses of fraction concepts, and yet had a 'gap' or missing link at almost the very 'start' of his understanding.

We'll return to Joe's story later in this chapter. It's a good example of how someone can become successful at higher mathematics with some obvious 'gaps' in much more basic aspects of the subject. And yet, one of the defining features of mathematics is that it builds, one idea leading to another, abstraction building on abstraction. The tree is often used as an image in education. People speak of the tree of knowledge. The tree has roots, which are required to make it grow; it has a solid foundation. It gets bigger year by year, grows upwards, through its central trunk, creating branches as it evolves. This image draws on a metaphor in which to learn is to build. And to build, you need a solid footing; you need to add to that ground floor layer by layer – you can't just jump to the tree-top or to the roof! And if ever there's a problem with the building, it's best to check its foundations and go back to the ground floor to make sure everything is stable, level and solid. Without the foundations, complicated mathematics can appear as an unknown and inaccessible world – and the mathematicians who work in this world like an alien species.

The idea that in order to learn something, you need to start with the simplest ideas and slowly build upwards – constructing one block at a time – seems to be common sense. The primary maths curriculum in schools in most countries in the West is designed with the tree idea in mind. It aims to lead students in a yearly spiral, touching on every topic and reaching a bit higher each year towards more complex concepts. Except, for some students, the spiral becomes more of a circle: returning to the same topics every year, perhaps gaining some fleeting insights, which are then forgotten; perhaps gaining skills which are lost in subsequent weeks. And perhaps, by the third or fourth time round the trunk, and encountering the same topic, a sense of self-preservation might kick in – why even bother this time? The top of the tree is moving out of sight. So when we're confused about something, is there an alternative to the instinct to try something simpler? Joe's experience hints at the fact that there might be.

To return to the botanical metaphors: what if our image of learning and mathematics was more like a mangrove forest than a single structure or tree? Mangroves grow as a decentralised network, each part dependent on other parts, growing upward and downward and sideways too. If there is a problem, no need to go back to the starting point; no need to find the trunk or the ground floor, since there is no one thing upon which everything else depends. Find a route that works for you. If maths were like that, how would it change your way of thinking about the curriculum? How would it change your way of addressing a child's or student's mistake? How would it change your feelings about your own mathematical understandings?

Tree

Mangrove forest

What if, to stretch the metaphors and images even further, there is something about learning and about mathematics that is like a tree *and* something that is like a mangrove forest? What might such alternative metaphors do to the sense, which we are labelling as a 'dogma', that maths learning is an activity of building blocks? A theme throughout this book is that there are some important insights in each dogma. In other words, there is something powerful in the idea of breaking down complicated problems into simpler ones, to help to solve them. But, when this idea of moving from simple to complicated becomes the only way to think (as we believe it has become) then it can inadvertently serve to make mathematics seem inaccessible, authoritative and alien. It can also isolate mathematical ideas, setting them up as singular trunks that must be learned on their own, one after another. Thinking in terms of mangrove forests draws attention to the interconnectedness of ideas and their mutual dependence on each other.

As a starting point to thinking through alternatives, we first want to consider some of the reasons behind the building block idea.

Learning as building blocks

It's certainly the case that if you tested a child's mathematical attainment as they grew, you'd find they can do more and more complicated things the older they get. In other words, what we can *do* appears to develop from simple to complicated. So, it surely makes sense to structure teaching to match this model of learning. And yet... the seeming obviousness of this idea can lead us to miss some of the nuances of how learning does and does not match teaching. If we look at young children learning how to speak, they grapple with significant complexity from the very start. So, while their growth in vocabulary might flow from simple to complex, the environment they're learning in is certainly not simple. This is why Seymour Papert spoke of the importance of inviting students to 'mathland' in the same way that we invite them to 'Frenchland' to learn French or 'Englishland' to learn English. These are 'lands' in which all aspects of the language ('up and down the tree') are present, not just simplified parts of it. Or, to take a more trivial example, when learning the rules of a new game, written or spoken instructions are often hard to follow – partly because we have little idea in our minds what's being referred to. What seems to work is to start off by playing the game with someone who's played it before, and to make sense of the rules through playing it. You can find yourself doing 'expert' things in your very first round of play. A sense of purpose and context speeds up how quickly we come to learn how to play.

The key point here is that environments which support rapid and engaging learning do not necessarily match that learning, in the sense of moving from simple to complex. We believe that the dogma that mathematics is a building block subject is in part a result of observing how competence and skill develop, and imagining this must mean that teaching tracks that development in a step-by-step or layer-by-layer way. In the case of maths, we believe that certain historical reasons, relating to the development of the subject, have influenced the idea that teaching must proceed step by step. In order to open ourselves to different possibilities, we trace some of these historical developments. This story begins in Egypt. It shows the precarity and chance around what insights and texts from past civilisations survive into future ones, and how easily other influences might have come to bear.

Alexandrian connections

Despite the fact he lived over 2,000 years ago, one of ancient Greece's mathematicians is still amazingly well known. His books are estimated to have had over 1,000 printed editions since printing began in the fifteenth century, second only to the Bible. They were studied in European universities across the world from the twelfth century and were part of the 'rediscovery' of ancient Greek texts in Europe that provoked the Renaissance. The ideas in the books still form part of a standard school maths curriculum and the books were studied directly in schools in the UK well into the twentieth century. They embody the very idea of tree mathematics. A deep mathematical conundrum arising from his ideas, linked to his so-called 'fifth postulate', was only resolved by mathematicians in the nineteenth century.[1]

The mathematician we're referring to is Euclid, who was born in Alexandria around 325 BCE, shortly after the founding of the city by Alexander the Great. It's believed that Euclid travelled widely in order to collect all of the known mathematical ideas he could find, which he collated in the 13 books of his *Elements* and in a series of other less well-known books. Although there's no existing copy that dates back to Euclid's time, a small number of translated versions of his *Elements* survived into modern times, thanks largely to Islamic mathematicians. We'll briefly sketch this history before getting to their contents.

At around the time of Euclid's birth, a library was founded in Alexandria that was to become known as the 'Great Library'. The intention of this library was to house *all* knowledge, an interesting parallel to Euclid's possible intention to gather together *all* known mathematics. The library helped the city become one of the intellectual centres of the Greek empire. The Great Library spawned some offshoots, likely as a result of running out of space. One of these, the 'Mouseion', outlasted the Library and is thought to have existed until 415CE, as a school. The last head of this school, and perhaps the most well-known female mathematician of the ancient era, was Hypatia (born around 370CE). Hypatia's father, Theon, wrote influential commentaries on Euclid's *Elements*, which means he created an edited, updated version. The first Arabic

---

[1] A postulate is an assumption that it's hoped will be readily accepted as true, without need for proof. For 2,000 years, mathematicians were concerned that the fifth postulate (that through a given point there is one and only one line that is parallel to a given line) did not seem obvious and they tried to prove it using the other four postulates. The resolution to the dilemma showed that the fifth postulate is equivalent to the assumption that our geometry is taking place on a flat and infinite plane. What was realised in the nineteenth century was that other geometries were possible (e.g. taking place on the surface of non-flat surfaces), and consistent with the first four postulates. In other words, the fifth postulate was a necessary assumption, not provable from the other four, in order to work with the geometry of the plane. The logic of this ancient Greek mathematician, it turns out, was impeccable.

translation of Euclid's *Elements* appears to have been written around 800CE by al-Hajjaj, whose Greek copy was obtained from Byzantium. Al-Hajjaj made two translations, and the second, shorter one is still in existence today. By the twelfth century the fate of Euclid's text was fairly secure. There were several versions in circulation, which were more or less elaborated from translations that related to Greek, Latin or Arabic originals. During the twelfth to fifteenth centuries the influence of the *Elements* in European universities grew. In the fifteenth century, Matteo Ricci, an Italian priest, travelled to China with a copy of the *Elements* and collaborated with the Chinese mathematician Xu Guangqi on a translation into Chinese. While the *Elements* survived into modern times through a small number of copies and had an incredible influence on teaching mathematics, another of Euclid's works, the three books of *Porisms*, has been lost. It is not quite clear what a 'Porism' was, but the indications are that these books focused on what would now be called projective geometry. The Western world might be a very different place if the projective geometry (which is all about relationships) in the books of *Porisms* had survived and the *Elements* (which, as we will see, set out hierarchies of thought) had been lost.

Euclid's *Elements*

The *Elements* are remarkable for the way they put mathematical ideas together. Things are presented in order, starting from the most basic notions and establishing truths which are then used to establish other, more complex truths. Euclid used what's now called the 'axiomatic method'. An 'axiom' in mathematics is a name for a starting assumption: an idea that's taken to be true in order to start thinking about something.

An analogy might help to give a sense of Euclid's method. Many computer games are structured into levels. Players must complete the first level before moving to the second. While completing the first level, the player often gains a tool that can be used at level 2. Such a design, perhaps unawares, follows the logic of Euclid's writing. He established some initial mathematical facts (level 1 of the 'game') and then arranged the next things to prove so that he could use what had been covered before (a bit like having a tool from level 1 to use at level 2). Having proved the next set of mathematical statements, he moved on to slightly more complex ones. You prove something and then you can add that to the set of truths you can draw on, in order to prove something else. Like computer games, which are often geared towards a final accomplishment, the *Elements* are sequenced so that it can be proved, at the very end, in the thirteenth book (!) that there are five and only five 'Platonic solids'.

The influence of Euclid and his *Elements* on European thought can hardly be overestimated. But the question we want to raise is whether this image of the subject as a set of 'truths' translates well to its learning. In a programme of logical deduction, a single flaw will compromise the whole system. An error in a proof, means not only is that proof now not proven, but also every other proof that makes use of it. However, when we think about teaching and learning something…

- Is it the case that you need to understand all the precursors of an idea before you can understand the idea itself?
- Does every idea have well-defined precursors?
- Do you have to understand an idea fully before you can use it in working on a more complex idea?
- Can you ever start in the middle?

The tree image of mathematics can be found also in the developmental progressions in the work of early psychologists such as Jean Piaget, where there is a first level of thinking that acts as a precursor to subsequent levels of thinking, with the levels tied to learners' chronological ages. While current developmental approaches do not rely as heavily on age, the tree imagery remains strong, with learning progressions that require getting to one given rung before being able to move onto the next.

We take up these questions in the remainder of this chapter. But first, we pick up the story from the start of this chapter, of Alf's work with Joe on fractions. This story offers a stark illustration that the dogma of mathematics as a building block subject is not the whole picture.

A story of fractions (Alf)

As a maths teacher, I taught for many years without ever being particularly aware of the ambiguity of mathematical symbols, for instance that '-2' can mean an object (e.g. a position on a number line) or a process (of subtracting 2). I wasn't aware of just how complex it must be for students when a teacher switches between different meanings while using the same symbol, but offering no clue that a shift has taken place. I imagine this must be part of what confused Joe in school. Maybe it's this kind of unmarked switching of meanings, with no change in the symbols to express those various meanings, which is one cause of anxiety of mathematics – a sense that you never quite know what is going on and that the rules might change at any moment. In fact, the subject is ambiguous rather than capricious – and that ambiguity can be laid bare for learners, for example by offering different images for the same symbols.

What helped Joe, in the end, was a realisation that there are two quite different ways of thinking about division. A fraction such as $\frac{500}{2}$ means 500 divided by 2. We can think about this as either relating to the question – 'How many 2s are there in 500?' – or as meaning that 500 is split into 2 parts, and asking how big one of those parts is. In other words, you could count up in 2s until you get to 500 to find how many steps of 2 are needed (250). Or, you could share 500 into 2 parts and find the size of one part (250). We can think about these issues in terms of lengths. It is actually remarkable that the two forms of division give the same answer, given that one image will be of 250 lengths of 2 making 500 and the second image will be of 2 lengths of 250.

In the first image, we start with 1 group of length 2 and ask how many 2s make 500. This can be written as follows:

1 : 2
? : 500

If one group has length 2, then you need 250 groups to make a length of 500.

In the second image, we start with 500 as being equivalent to 2 groups and ask how big one group would be. This can be written:

500 : 2
? : 1

If 500 is the length of 2 (equal) groups, then 250 is the length of 1 group.

The two versions of division can be applied to the fraction Joe was confused about, with different images. The first one would suggest: count up in one-third until you get to 2 and find out how many steps of one-third are needed. The markings on the number line below are 'thirds'; three steps of one third get us to 1 and a further three steps get us to 2, so Joe's fraction is equivalent to 6. The diagram below was one of the images that helped Joe.

In terms of the second version of division, we think about 2 as equivalent to the length of $\frac{1}{3}$ of a group, and we need to find the length of 1 whole group.

$2 : \frac{1}{3}$

$? : 1$

I remember Joe being particularly struck that the answer (6) doesn't even appear on the number line above.

Joe's case suggests that mathematics need *not* be a building block subject, in terms of how it is learnt. Or, at the very least, Joe shows that it's possible to gain a sophisticated understanding of a concept, while lacking some significant ideas about that very same concept. If Joe's teachers had noticed his difficulties with fractions and never offered him more complex ideas until he had grasped the presumed basic ones, he might never have progressed on to PhD level.

Joe's story raises the question of whether humans learn *well* in a building block way. It is clear that you *can* learn in this way since this is how many of us were taught maths, but the questions are:

- Is this a sensible way of organising learning?
- Are there alternatives?

These questions are pressing given how many people worldwide seem to struggle to understand school mathematics.

Dealing with complexity

One educationalist we will refer to in several chapters is Caleb Gattegno, so it's useful to say a few words about him here. He was born in Alexandria in 1911 and died in 1988. He achieved some fame in his lifetime for his ideas about teaching and learning, including popularising Cuisenaire rods across the world in the 1960s. These colourful rectangular-shaped rods with lengths ranging from 1 cm to 10 cm are still used in some primary schools. Gattegno helped to set up an influential organisation in the UK called the Association of Teachers of Mathematics and developed ideas for the entire school curriculum, in particular for mathematics and languages.

Gattegno took the study of how children learned their home language seriously. One observation he made was that there is a phase around the age of three when children learning English make grammatical errors along the lines of saying things like 'I runned' instead of 'I ran'. Gattegno took this to mean that we don't learn our home language by imitation alone (children are unlikely to have heard anyone say 'I runned'). Instead, the phrase 'I runned' seems to show that children notice a pattern and (over-)apply it. In other words, to say 'I runned', a child must have noticed a pattern of contexts and word endings (that we add '-ed' to indicate past tense) and then must have generalised this pattern and applied it to the verb 'to run', without realising the verb is irregular. Generalising and applying rules in unfamiliar situations are usually taken to be higher-level skills, only available to much older learners. If we were designing environments for learning a home language, it's unlikely (on spiral curriculum lines) we would ever imagine that three-year-olds were capable of such thinking. And yet, it seems such thinking is perhaps central to how children come to be creative with language. The complexity of the home language environment, for most children, means there are multiple and overlapping patterns available to be noticed and tried out. The environment (in the form of other children and adults) provides feedback that helps hone awareness of new vocabulary and grammar. There is no sense that a child can't move onto an awareness of more complex or different forms of grammar because they haven't mastered one particular grammatical aspect.

Of course there are neurological differences between three-year-olds, adolescents and adults, but the ability to generalise is surely not something that ever goes away, and it's a skill for which there's good evidence that pre-school age children are highly adept. However, there are obvious organisational and contextual differences between ways of learning in schools and how children learn their home language, so perhaps there are reasons not to look to this example for inspiration. There have been attempts to try to explain away the exceptional feat of learning our home language. One popular idea is that we're born with some kind of 'universal grammar', though this is now rejected by its key author, Noam Chomsky. Another idea is that children's brains have a plasticity that is lost as people get older. This does seem to be an accepted fact of brain development, but the biggest drop in connectivity occurs during early adolescence, so changes in brain plasticity alone don't seem to account for differences in how children learn as they move from the age of, say, four to fourteen. And yet there are often marked differences in terms of the ease and enjoyment of learning a home language and the sometimes tortuous and laboured learning in school. Gattegno was interested in what is possible in terms of the efficiency, or economy, of learning.

It feels as though we may be scared about the idea that we could learn as quickly as we did when we were children and so we try to find explanations for how it's not possible. Gattegno's astonishing claim was that we still possess all of those powers of the mind that allowed us to learn our home language and we can use them right now in terms of our own learning, and in order to structure the learning of children. So, what might some of these powers be?

When learning their home language, children show they can identify specific features of complex situations, e.g. noticing individual words from within the stream of speech. They notice and stress some things, while ignoring others – 'stressing and ignoring' is one of the powers Gattegno highlighted. Children are supported in noticing patterns by adults and others who give them feedback and who themselves stress specific aspects of the complex environment – pattern-spotting is another power. Being creative within a given constraint or structure is also a power: from the start of their learning, children produce language for the purpose of communication; they innovate and create new speech. Another power we'd suggest is an awareness of inverse relations. For instance, children navigate with ease the complementary relations that 'I am your child' means 'You are my parent'. And, for Gattegno, these powers of the mind exist before language. A direct implication for learning mathematics is that we can draw on children's awareness of 'doing and undoing', by always working with processes and their inverses together (e.g. teaching addition and subtraction together, multiplication and division, factorising and expanding).

Gattegno proposed that the mathematics curriculum should be ordered in terms of a sequence of awarenesses to be mastered. He rejected other principles for ordering, such as according to the history of ideas (an idea Steiner adopted for his Waldorf curriculum), or according to logic (as per Euclid) or a spiral curriculum (an idea from Jerome Bruner, influential in the West, that the curriculum should return to the same content each year but go deeper each time). Gattegno turned 'awareness' into a countable noun, writing about 'awarenesses', i.e. items or moments of awareness. An example of an awareness could be the sense that division can be thought about in two different ways (as per Joe's story above). In this case, for that awareness to be useful, there are a number of other associated awarenesses needed – for instance, images associated with the two conceptions or perhaps procedures associated with them. Interestingly, curriculum-ordering in China and Japan has some features of organisation by awareness, in the sense that there is attention to the development of awareness of mathematical structures (such as models of how a whole can be split into parts) before attention to procedures and routines. Sometimes starting with something seemingly complex can make learning simpler for a learner than starting with what experienced learners think of as a basic building block. Sometimes, building blocks only make sense if you have an image already of the whole system. The image of learning as a mangrove forest perhaps helps disrupt a sense of there being an obvious place to begin.

In the next chapter, we'll look at how the dogma and the alternative approach might work in practice, by looking specifically at teaching algebra.

Putting into practice A: Early learning of algebra

Algebra is often a watershed in many people's experience of school mathematics. In many curricula around the world algebra appears relatively late on. In the history of mathematics, algebra made its appearance centuries after the development of ideas about number. In terms of building blocks, it seems obvious that algebra needs to come after number, i.e. we learn about number and then we generalise to ideas of algebra.

And yet, if we look at mathematics in terms of awareness as in Dogma A, and if we take the idea of how we learn the language of our home seriously, we may be led to some surprising conclusions. Before offering a case study of the teaching and learning of algebra, it is perhaps useful to say a little about what we are taking algebra to mean. Algebra is often expressed through the use of letters. The mystery begins right there – what on earth does this x mean? Statements such as 'it stands for *any* number' don't always seem to help. Perhaps one of the difficulties is that x is often used to stand for something unknown; it's a way of symbolising what we do not know. Although one surprising thing is that, by giving a precise label to what we do not know, we can often find a way of coming to know it. It turns out that working with what we do not know, as if we know it, is quite a common human activity, and one which children would recognise.

The essence of algebra is the awareness of relationships. An expression such as $x+y$ expresses a relationship between two things – the relationship is that they are added. What can be confusing is that when we're working algebraically, we are not interested in the result of this addition, but in the relationship between the two. Children who are used to mathematical questions always having an answer can find this disturbing. An expression like $x+y$ needs to be 'held' somehow. It is pending. There is nothing that can be done with it, except noting the way in which x and y are combined. The expression can only be evaluated if we're told that x and y have specific number values. Algebra is used to express relationships that have been observed or that are needed for some other purpose.

For anyone used to maths resulting in definite answers, the unfinished nature of an algebraic expression can sometimes cause unease. The same goes for the way a single expression can have countless results, depending on the values of x and y. There's no way to pin down or stabilise algebra, except in a particular situation. The lack of a result combines with the seeming abstractness of algebraic symbols to create this puzzlement around what on earth the symbols refer to. This chapter will show that there's no need for algebra to seem otherworldly or remote.

If we try not to be held back by how maths has always been taught and instead look at the awarenesses involved in working with algebra and working with number, we may be led to the conclusion that Caleb Gattegno reached: that work on algebra can successfully come *first*. Indeed, there is an age, usually before children are four or five, when they can often quite happily say what you get if you add 'one apple' and 'one apple' (two apples) but are stumped by the question 'What is one plus one?'. This observation suggests that children first make sense of number names as adjectives. We imagine a child at this age might be able to answer, 'What is one unit plus one unit?', or even, 'What is one hundred plus one hundred?'. The awareness of a number as a thing in itself, or an object, seems to come *after* the sense of number as something applied to other things (like apples). If numbers are treated as attributes or adjectives, then they are vehicles of comparison. In other words, children's first encounters with number, through learning their home language, bear some of the hallmarks of algebra, in the sense that they are about relationships between things, not the things in themselves.

Gattegno developed a curriculum in which children work on relationships between lengths of rods (less than, more than, equal to) and express these relationships using letters, before they move on to working with numerals. In other words, the curriculum sequence begins with awarenesses of algebra, and uses those awarenesses in order to develop awarenesses of number. There are resources and examples of this sequencing being used with spectacular effect, for example, Gattegno (1963) and Gattegno (1974). The contemporary Russian educator

Vasily Davydov also suggested that children work on relationships, expressed algebraically, before they encounter number. For Davydov, the basis of the initial work on relationship was measurement. And for Gattegno, it was the lengths of rectangular rods. Davydov's ideas have been implemented with remarkable success in Russia and elsewhere, including inspiring a research programme in the USA called Measure Up.

The success of the Davydov and Gattegno curriculum approach raises the question of why every curriculum isn't doing this. We think that the weight of how mathematics has traditionally been taught, going back to the influence of Euclid's *Elements* across Europe and beyond, means that it would require a significant sustained effort to make these wholesale changes, requiring extensive training for teachers. (We've learnt from previous wholesale curriculum changes that support for teachers is critical.) Of course, children can and do learn mathematics through approaching number before algebra. And there are systems using the more traditional order, for example in East Asia, where it seems like the curriculum organisation and teaching leads to high levels of success for the majority of students. The point we really want to make is that the fact that it's possible to work with ideas of algebra *before* number shows that mathematics is *not*, or is *not only*, a building block subject. There are many ways to build mathematical understanding. In fact, the metaphor of building doesn't seem to be particularly helpful. As we have said, perhaps a more accurate image of learning mathematics is the mangrove metaphor from Dogma A, in which parts interact and combine but there is no clearly defined hierarchy. What this means is that there's no good rationale for denying some children access to aspects of school mathematics: just because some children find number work hard, that's no reason not to teach them algebra. In fact, it might well be the children who struggle with number who get on better with algebra – because procedural calculations rarely need to be carried out. This also brings into question the practice of separating children into 'ability' groups according to their prior attainment. This is a point that also comes up in subsequent chapters.

Case studies of practice

There are current examples of primary schools arranging their teaching in order to work with students' awarenesses and engage the powers of the mind, while working within their respective curriculums. At one school in south-west England, Caroline Ainsworth revitalised all of the mathematics teaching with spectacular results – she won a national Teacher of the Year award in 2015. She has written about her approach (Ainsworth, 2016) and been interviewed for England's National Centre for Excellence in the Teaching of Mathematics (NCETM). Caroline made use of Cuisenaire rods (see image below) in all classes, from Reception (ages 4–5) to Year 6 (ages 10–11). She developed her approach to teaching mathematics over many years, drawing inspiration from Gattegno's ideas as well as the work of the Canadian teacher Madeleine Goutard (see Goutard, 1964 and www.youtube.com/watch?v=Kw94gmzRrOY).

Caroline found that the rods provided consistent imagery for her students, such that the rods became tools that allowed them to gain an intuitive grasp of mathematical transformations. It's important that children are given time to explore and become familiar with the rods by themselves, if they are going to be used in an ongoing manner. Gattegno himself advised periods of ten to 20 minutes of free play with the rods for Reception-age children, extending for weeks or even months, before intervening. During this time, colour names can be slowly introduced for the rods.

After a time of free play with the rods, children can be invited to make 'trains' by placing rods end to end, and then asked to describe their trains using colour names. A train might be made up of w y y r (white, yellow, yellow and then red rods). The '+' sign can be introduced, so that the train is described as: w + y + y + r. Notice that there is no 'answer' here, no equals sign; just a description with letters. This supports children in making meaning of strings of algebra-looking symbols and getting used to there not needing to be an answer.

It's a natural activity for children to compare the lengths of different trains and when the symbols <, > and = are introduced, a whole new world opens. Children can now express what they know about the rods, for instance: g + r + y < o + p. Again, there are no numbers involved in making such statements, no arriving at a single answer and no counting. Eventually, children may focus on making two trains of the same length, for example: t + w = d + g.

At this stage, the children might not be seen as doing algebra – they are simply using letter names for lengths. However, from this basis, algebraic thinking develops. There are several possibilities for development and a number of different schemes or textbooks which cover these (e.g. see Gattegno, 1963).

One avenue is to look at 'staircases' of rods; another is to explore the different ways two rods can be combined to make the same particular length, as below.

A relationship can be observed – the shorter one rod gets, the longer the other one gets: b + w = d + r = y + g = p + p = g + y = r + d = w + b.

Considerable and complex mathematics can arise from looking at the different ways of making particular lengths using two rods, or three rods, and so on. Various questions can be explored, such as how many arrangements with two rods are possible. Looking at results for other rods, it is possible to generalise (there is only one arrangement for the red rod, which has length two; there are two arrangements of the light green rod, which is length three). Perhaps for any length rod, we could predict the number of arrangements that are possible, using two other rods. Generalisation is a mathematical activity often seen as complex and inaccessible and yet, in meaningful contexts, it can be straightforward.

Another avenue of development comes from looking at when two of the same rod has the same length as a single rod. For example, $p + p = t$. From this situation, numerals can be introduced. If $p + p = t$, then we can say that $2p = t$ and, as a direct result, or as an alternative expression, that $p = \frac{1}{2} t$.

Once children start making transformations among the statements they write, then they can be truly said to be engaging in algebraic thinking. Caroline Ainsworth has shown the way in which the rods support her students' understanding of fractions, perceived as relationships between lengths of rods.

The introduction of numerals is significant and is done in a way that isn't immediately obvious, as well as being counter to many current primary curricula around the world. When children write $2p = t$, they may be looking at concrete materials (two purple rods laid against a brown rod). The letter symbols are attached to something visible and tangible. However, the numeral '2' describes the relationship between the rods; it isn't a label for a rod in itself. And in this subtle shift of focus lies the basis for the entire power of a Gattegno-inspired approach.

While a shift in the curriculum to deal with algebra before arithmetic may not be possible in many school contexts, the idea of using concrete materials in a way that focuses on the abstract relationships between them is one that can be used in any area of the curriculum. It's common for children in primary education to need concrete materials. But to us, what often seems to be missed is how children can work with those concrete materials while considering abstract relations. For instance, when introducing measurement, it's common to focus on what '1 cm' or '1 metre' is and have concrete examples of these lengths. However, a focus on relationships would mean starting with children measuring one length using another length. So for instance, the classroom wall might be 20 books long, while the book might be 12 coins long. An awareness develops about how lengths can be described by other lengths, and how the variety of measures means a standard measurement is needed (see McGuire & Evans (2018) for a classroom example of developing a need for standard measurement, based on the children's book *Aliens Love Underpants*). Similarly, when introducing any mathematical operation (addition, etc.) a focus on relationships would mean working with the operation and its inverse at the same time (addition and subtraction, multiplication and division). If a situation involves an addition, there must be a description of the same situation which involves a subtraction. It's possible to work on how these different, inverse descriptions relate to each other, before engaging in the mechanics of the operations themselves.

An example of working on addition and subtraction before counting comes from Davydov's curriculum ideas, which are being used in Hawaii among other places (Curriculum Research & Development Group, University of Hawai'i at Mānoa, unknown). By comparing lengths, or areas, or volumes, or weights, children use labels for shapes and write A > B for situations like the one below.

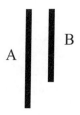

They will be encouraged to write the inverse statement, that B < A. Over time, a third element will be introduced, the length (or area, volume, weight) that you need to add to B to get A. In other words, if A > B, then we can find a third measure, C, so that A = B + C. And from here, children are again encouraged to write the relationship in all the different ways possible:

$$B = A - C \text{ and } C = A - B.$$

Children work on the relations between addition, subtraction and equality, without actually carrying out any additions or subtractions (in the sense of using numbers).

We know from the work of teachers in Hawaii, and teachers such as Ainsworth, Goutard and Gattegno, that there can be no difficulty for children aged four or five to express relations such as A = B + C and associated statements, or 2p = t and the inverse, ½ t = p. This is particularly the case in social and classroom contexts that are fairly stable, and when those children have not been categorised into levels of 'ability', a practice which all too often becomes self-fulfilling. An archive film of Gattegno teaching demonstrates such work (National Film Board of Canada, 1961). The surprising way in which fractions can be made concrete is by using the fraction notation to show what isn't concrete, i.e. to show the relations between the rods rather than the rods themselves. Designing contexts where mathematical symbols appear as relationships allows children to use what they know, from living their lives, about doing and undoing – dealing both with relations and their inverse helps their understanding. Any relationship can be experienced or expressed from at least two points of view.

When approaching mathematics through the use of Cuisenaire rods, it is no more complex for a child to write 2p = t than it is for that child to write ½ t = p. The expressions capture the same relationship. The apparent ease with which children within this curriculum come to use and work with fractions is in stark contrast to typical experience. It's one of the advantages of a curriculum organisation which begins with general, algebraic awarenesses about lengths and their combinations before moving to considering number. It's also worth saying that there's little need for children to be counting in the early stages – for more on this, see Putting into practice E.

Choices in curriculum organisation

We can look to the USA for more evidence of the potential for alternative approaches to mathematics in the primary curriculum. The Bronx Better Learning (BBL) Charter Schools in New York were set up along the lines of Gattegno's curriculum, which they follow in mathematics. A report from 2019 indicated that, in mathematics, 78 per cent of BBL's students in grades 3 to 8 scored at or above what is classified as a 'proficient' level, compared with 35 per cent of students in the same grades in other schools in the district (Bronx Charter Schools for Better Learning); in other words, more than double the proportion of students across the district. The school consistently achieves this while serving some of the most disadvantaged students in the district.

At the very least, these examples show that there are many routes to becoming successful at mathematics and many ways to build maths skills. They indicate that there might be a significant advantage to tackling topics often seen as complex, such as algebra and fractions, early in the primary curriculum, if this is done with the support of consistent representations. The work done on the Measure Up programme in Hawaii has shown how children can develop sophisticated understandings of place value, through a focus on measurement.

In England, the UK government (as of 2021) endorses a 'mastery' approach to primary mathematics. One of the powerful ideas is that teachers work with a limited set of representations of number and use them consistently throughout the primary years. (This can be seen in Professional Development materials for teachers published on the NCETM website.) For example, there is a suggestion of making consistent use of a number line image, and of consistent ways of showing how two parts make a whole. The mastery approach, as envisioned within the NCETM Professional Development resources, also involves reordering the National Curriculum content. This reordering has been done, in part, with a view to the learners' awareness and of offering a coherent route through the primary curriculum. While these resources do not quite go as far as proposing algebra before arithmetic, they do suggest working with lengths and measures as a starting point of the curriculum, in line with Gattegno's ideas. As a parent, or teacher, or learner, you may be inspired by this blog, written by a mother using Gattegno's mathematical materials with her child: www.arithmophobianomore.com/category/how-to-teach.

Summary

Dogma A and Putting into practice A traced the idea that 'Maths is a building block subject' to the defining work of the ancient Greek mathematician Euclid. There is a sense in which mathematics, as a subject, can be arranged in a logical sequence that starts with the most basic ideas and gets progressively more complex. This sequencing is powerful if the intention is to prove or justify each step and claim along the way. However, a sequence that works best for logic is not necessarily a sequence that is productive for learning. Moreover, the sequence that works better for old technology (paper-and-pencil) is not necessarily productive for today's learners, who have access to tools like Cuisenaire rods. Instead, Caleb Gattegno proposed sequencing the curriculum in terms of awareness and, in particular, that awarenesses of algebra can come before awarenesses of number. Caroline Ainsworth's teaching demonstrates how powerful this approach can be in a contemporary context. A key idea is that students *can* work on relationships between numbers as a way into understanding number. This isn't to say that they need to do this to make sense of mathematics, but rather that there's good evidence that, if we can make relationships visible or tangible to children, then they are able to work with abstract mathematical ideas about those relationships. Our belief, which is a theme through other chapters, is that a focus on relationships can make learning mathematics engaging and effective. Ultimately, what is important to us is not to find a 'best' curriculum organisation, but to realise that there's no such thing as best organisation, and that there are many possible routes to understanding mathematics which we need to keep exploring.

One thing that arguments about whether a curriculum should begin with algebra or begin with number show is that there is a genuine question and choice here. If it's accepted that there may be multiple, and sometimes quite opposite, routes to successful learning, then one practice that is definitely not justified is denying students the opportunity to work on more complex ideas because they have not understood something those ideas make use of. In other words, the practice of streaming or setting in schools, in which students who are struggling go more slowly and keep returning to the same content, is based on a flawed dogma. In the UK, there have been recent moves away from grouping students according to perceived ability, particularly at primary school level. However, the practice of setting at secondary level remains widespread.

It may be that students *need* what is seen as a more complex set of ideas, in order to make sense of the ideas considered to be the basics. Human learning appears to thrive on working with complexity, as with language learning at home. Rather than an image of learning maths as a tree, or constructing a building brick by brick from bottom to top, we might have an image of a mangrove forest, or growing a root system. Different aspects nurture each other and there is no obvious hierarchy in terms of what is most or least important.

Dogma B: 'Maths is always right or wrong'

Nathalie's story

When I was nine, I remember riding in our pick-up truck, squeezed between my parents in the front seat. I asked my mother how far we were from our destination and she read off the distance from the map, in miles. Canada had recently converted from the imperial to the metric system, but our maps were old. When I asked for the kilometre equivalent, she responded at what seemed to me like lightning speed. How had she done it so quickly? I knew the conversion involved multiplying by some complicated number – not a whole one – as my teachers had drilled us for years prior to the changeover with equivalence charts and rules. So I believed this wasn't something you did in your head; shouldn't she have needed at least a pencil and paper?

She soon explained. There was no need to bother with the actual conversion factor, something like 1.609. Instead, you just rounded to 1.6, which was just the same thing as 1 + 0.5 + 0.1. And that made the conversion more like a walk in the park. Take the number of miles, say 40, then add half that number, and then one-tenth of it (just take off the last zero!) to get 40 + 20 + 4. So 40 miles was near enough 64 kilometres, an answer my father confirmed with the speedometer. I was so impressed. We tried her method with a few more imaginary destinations.

What I learned that day was that maths was not just a set of rules that produced correct answers, but it could also be a tool to help me figure things out – and that I could use that tool as I saw fit. In a way, 64 is the wrong answer; but in another way, it was as right as we needed it to be. My mother had used the same operations I was learning in school. But she used them as tools to suit her own purposes. She had not only rounded the troublesome conversion factor – with a brash gusto I had not encountered in school, though very much admired – but she also turned the 1.6 into a new thing (1 + 0.5 + 0.1) that gave it new power, new usefulness.

The dogma 'Maths is always right or wrong' can be a source of relief and comfort for some people. In a world that's constantly changing, some dependability is often welcome. We can count on the sum of 40 and 20 being 60; on half of 40 being 20. This may feel comforting, especially in our current post-truth era, during which the status of almost every fact seems to depend on your political affiliations. It can also be satisfying to know, after working on a problem for a while and arriving at a solution, that you were right.

Yet, for many people, there's something authoritarian about mathematics (and its teachers and textbooks); not only are there right or wrong answers, but there are preordained rules for getting the right ones. And, as this quotation suggests, this rule-like behaviour also determines who will be seen as 'good' at maths:

> 'And on the eighth day, God created mathematics. He took stainless steel, and he rolled it out thin, and he made it into a fence forty cubits high, and infinite cubits long. And on this fence, in fair capitals, he did print rules, theorems, axioms and pointed reminders. "Invert and multiply"; "The square on the hypotenuse is three decibels louder than one hand clapping"; "Always do what's in the parentheses first." And when he was finished, he said, "On one side of the fence will reside those who are good at math. And on the other will remain those who are bad at math, and woe unto them, for they shall weep and gnash their teeth."' (Buerk, 1982, p. 19).

As it turns out, this dogma can be challenged, and in many different ways, but it's worth understanding where it comes from and why it's become so prevalent in contemporary culture, particularly in schooling.

From Truth to truths in mathematics

The mathematical view of truth has been shaped, in large part, by the deductive system of logic demonstrated in Euclid's *Elements* (see Dogma A).

The logic goes like this. First, start with a few simple assumptions, which you might even consider to be intuitively true. This is like starting with a small number of piano notes that sound good together. Next, combine the assumptions and look for a pattern. This might be like combining notes into chords and then sequences of chords. Then, show how this new pattern must follow from the basic assumption. So, if we know that C and E sound good together and E and G sound good together, then playing C, E, and G will be a new combination that sounds good too. And from there, you can start composing complex melodies. In maths, you can create more and more patterns just like how in music you can create more and more songs. And what is true in maths, that is, what can be derived from the basic assumptions, is kind of like what sounds good in music.

In music, however, we know that what sounds good can change over time. We even know that what sounds good to people from one culture might not sound good to others. Surprisingly, a very similar thing can happen in maths. The basic assumptions are just that: assumptions. If you start with other assumptions, it can lead to entirely different patterns, just like other combinations of notes can lead to different genres of music. It can even happen that the patterns actually contradict each other, which is exactly what happened in the nineteenth century in mathematics. First, there was Euclid's 'castle', his work. But then, mathematicians discovered they could make other castles too. As soon as there are two castles, it is hard to continue believing in *the* truth. In other words, what emerged as true was that there could be many truths.

Let's look at a very specific example. In Euclid's castle, if you measure all three angles of a triangle, you will find that their sum is always exactly 180°. But when a triangle is drawn on a sphere (spherical geometry), the sum of the angles of a triangle is not only always bigger than 180°, but changes depending on the size of the triangle. For example, imagine drawing a triangle on the earth's surface that connects the North Pole to a point on the equator in South America and to another one in Africa, as in the figure on page 30. Start at the North Pole and 'walk' all the way down to the point in South America, then turn 90° in order to walk along the equator towards Africa. Then, turn 90° to complete your trek back up to the North Pole. So, two of the angles of your triangle already add up to 180°, let alone the third angle, which will be much more than 90° and could even be up to 180°. By contrast, if you walked counterclockwise around a triangle drawn on a field, the sum of the three angles would only be a tiny bit larger than 180° because that triangle is actually on the curved lines of the surface of the earth.

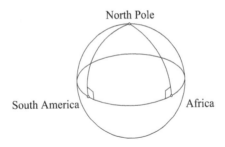

North Pole

South America

Africa

So, if you say the sum of the angles of a triangle is 180°, are you right or wrong? Prior to the nineteenth century, you would have been right, no questions asked. But since then, you would be right, *assuming that* you were referring to a triangle on a plane rather than on the surface of a sphere. In other words, your assertion is locally but not globally true. Another way of saying this is that truths are contingent – they depend on the assumptions you make. In this sense, there is no capital T truth, because every statement depends on assumptions. We have only specified two sets of assumptions here, but it turns out that there are many (you can draw triangles on doughnut-shaped objects too!). In addition, there's no reason to believe that we've run out of new assumptions to make.

We feel that it's unfortunate that most pupils never encounter these new geometries (shapes on a sphere or on doughnut-shaped objects, for example), unless they pursue a higher education degree in mathematics, because it means they can go through 12 years of maths education without encountering the difference between Truth and truth – without experiencing how a simple change in assumptions can totally change the facts that can be derived from them.

However, there are other situations in school mathematics that might not be as historically dramatic, but that still exemplify the sense of contingency. For example, when pupils shift from working with whole numbers (1, 2, 3, 4, ...) to working with integers (...-3, -2, -1, 0, 1, 2, 3, ...), they meet the idea that a fact about numbers – that you cannot subtract a larger number from a smaller one – is suddenly contradicted. Perhaps instead of saying, 'Well, we were just lying to you before because you were too young to understand negative numbers', we might say, 'It's true that you cannot subtract a larger number from a smaller one *when assuming* you're working with whole numbers.' This could shift students' perspectives about maths being right and wrong by helping them appreciate that the status of any statement depends on the assumptions being made. This might sound like it would only be accessible to older pupils, but children develop the kind of 'if... then... logic' used in assumption-making at a very young age, when they contend with parental admonitions of the kind, 'If you eat your dinner, then you can have dessert'!

Are there truths at all?

At the turn of the twentieth century, after the debacle around Euclidean geometry, which mathematicians felt could no longer count as the emblem of Truth in mathematics, there was a turn to number and to logic as the more secure foundations – if geometry was too tied up with human perception, then maybe arithmetic might be less subject to interpretation. This project failed and led to an even greater drama in maths that threatened the very idea of mathematical truth. It happened in 1931.

The drama boils down to this: if you come up with a set of assumptions, *any* set of assumptions, then there will be some statements or claims or patterns that can neither be proven nor disproven. This is scary for a mathematician. And that's not all. It also turned out that it would be impossible to be sure that all of the patterns that seemed to be true would not contradict each other at some point. To give you a sense of what this felt like for mathematicians, it was like looking up a word in the dictionary and not being able to tell whether it is actually a word or not and, at the same time, not knowing whether the definition of that word contradicted the definition of another word. While that might be bearable in the constantly changing, constantly evolving world of language, it was a blow to the mathematical fantasy, because it put limits on the possibility of attaining Truth.

Before we go further, we want to make sure we do not overstep the implications of the 1931 drama, which were caused by the work of the mathematician Kurt Gödel. Mathematicians still strongly believe that when they prove a theorem, they are asserting a Truth. Moreover, mathematicians have developed many techniques and practices that ensure that their proofs are as true as possible. This means that even though they can no longer assert that they are absolutely True, it does mean that they are exceedingly convincing. Mathematicians probably agree more with each other about mathematical statements than most other professions. This has led a good number of philosophers of mathematics to describe mathematics truths as extremely reliable conjectures, constantly being verified and validated in a wide range of situations by a large number of people.

Therefore, while we can find situations in which 2 + 2 does not equal 4 within mathematics (if, for example, we are working in a base-4 world, which means we use only the four digits 0, 1, 2, and 3, and each place value tells us the number of 1s, 4s, 16s, etc. – in the same way that our base-10 tells us the number of 1s, 10s, 100s, etc. – then the number after 3 is 10 because we have one unit of 4 and 0 units of 1^1), as well as outside of mathematics (2 oranges and 2 apples do not make 4 apples or 4 oranges or even 4 apple-oranges), there is no denying that 4 is the desired answer on the maths worksheet. (That said, if a pupil responded by saying, 'It depends what base you are working in', we would happily give full marks to them!) But it turns out that there are many mathematical activities in which we might want to engage pupils that do not fit the right–wrong paradigm, as we will discuss in the next section.

For now, though, let's just consider how the right/wrong binary can be imagined as a kind of balance with two sides. Right or wrong. Either/or. The image of the balance applies to many other binaries, such as male/female and mind/body and culture/nature. More generally, this spatial imagery – an image we use to make sense of the world – encourages us to think that things come in two kinds, and that these kinds are distinct from each other or in opposition to each other. We can challenge this spatial imaginary by evoking the image of a ceiling mobile, where things might come in threes or fours, and not just in twos. In our case, instead of right *or* wrong, we might admit other kinds. Like the conversion of

---

[1] So instead of the base-ten count of 0, 1, 2, 3, 4, 5, 6, 7, 8, 9, 10, 11, ... we would have 0, 1, 2, 3, 10 (4x1 + 0), 11 (4x1+1), 12 (4x1+2), 13 (4x1+3), 20 (4x2+0), 21 (4x2+1), 22 (4x2+2), 23 (4x2+3), ...

40 miles into 64 kilometres, things can be adequate or, like the sum of the angles of a triangle, things can be contingent.

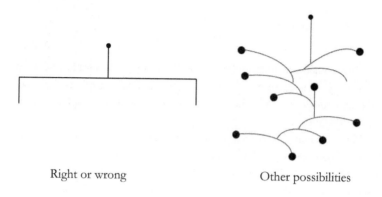

Right or wrong   Other possibilities

From giving answers to asking questions

In their book *The Art of Problem Posing*, Stephen Brown and Marion Walter argue that one of the most important parts of doing mathematics is posing problems (Brown & Walter, 2005). We've become accustomed to problem-solving in the mathematics classroom, but you cannot solve a problem that has not first been posed. If pupils feel that maths follows the rules of God, as the quotation at the beginning of the chapter hinted, then it is perhaps in part because they've only ever been asked to solve problems posed by the authority figures of the maths classroom, namely textbooks or teachers.

While the solution to a problem might be judged right or wrong, it is much harder to use this binary logic on the problem itself. Indeed in maths, a problem is judged by how 'good' it is. Here is a problem considered very good: every even number greater than 2 is the sum of two prime numbers. This problem is called the Goldbach Conjecture, named after the eighteenth-century mathematician, Christian Goldbach. It hasn't yet been proved, hence why it is called a conjecture rather than a theorem. Try it out.

$$4 = 2 + 2$$
$$6 = 5 + 1$$

$$8 = 5 + 3$$
$$10 = 5 + 5$$
$$12 = 7 + 5$$
$$\ldots$$
$$100 = 53 + 47$$
$$\ldots$$

The conjecture is considered 'good' because it is simple and easy to state, plus, after only a little experimentation, it seems to be true. Mathematicians also like the fact that despite being so simple, it's very difficult to prove.

What Brown and Walter do is show how easy (and fun) it can be to pose your own problems using their 'what-if-not?' method. So, for example, instead of using the word 'even' in Goldbach's conjecture, we used the word 'odd' ('what-if-not even')? What can we say about odd numbers in terms of the sum of prime numbers? Let's try it out:

$$5 = 2 + 3$$
$$7 = 2 + 5$$
$$9 = 2 + 7$$
$$11 = \cancel{2+9} = \cancel{3+8} = \cancel{4+7} = \cancel{5+6}$$

Well, it seems that the new conjecture isn't true since it fails for 11, as all of the sums written above include at least one non-prime number. But, we could do this:

$$11 = 2 + 2 + 7$$
$$13 = 3 + 3 + 7$$
$$15 = 5 + 5 + 5$$
$$17 = 5 + 5 + 7$$
$$19 = 5 + 7 + 7$$

So far, so good. These odd numbers can be written as the sum of three prime numbers. Does it work for 99 or 101?

It's easy to get carried away posing problems – like we just did! – and that's exactly what mathematicians do. They vary statements, try things out, find a pattern and then make conjectures, which they then try to prove. Some pupils find it much more interesting to solve problems that they themselves have come up with, rather than solving problems from the textbook or the teacher. Just as importantly, by posing their own problems, pupils can gain appreciation for where problems come from, which can help them improve their own mathematical understanding – generating sums of prime numbers requires them to develop a strong fluency with prime numbers, for example.

Problem-posing can also occur around so-called real-world situations. For example, a problem typically posed to pupils in primary school is the following: 'Bonnie has 24 metres of fencing and wants to create an enclosed rectangular garden that is as big as possible. What will be the dimensions of her garden?' Solving this problem in a strictly mathematical sense involves working with perimeter and area. If the perimeter of the garden must be 24 metres, then the largest garden will be when the length of each side of the rectangle is 6 metres.

Thinking about real gardens, however, might lead to a host of new problems. For example, what-if-not rectangular? What other shapes might work well for gardens? What-if-not biggest? Perhaps Bonnie wants to have a garden that is just the right size for her needs, so she wants a smaller one than the maximum size possible. What should Bonnie do if her neighbour gives her 3 more metres of extra fencing? What if Bonnie's land has an obstruction on it that needs to be taken into account? All of these questions, which pupils can and will ask – if invited – can lead to new problems. One thing we appreciate very much about these new problems is that they show how perfect mathematical formulas and techniques (calculating perimeter, maximising area) are often insufficient for solving problems in the real world. Such problems are often more complex, and therefore cannot be solved on a single axis of right–wrong, but might involve other considerations as well, including botanical, aesthetic and ethical ones.

Asking different questions, listening in different ways

Most of the right/wrong logic of school maths is associated with arithmetic, especially at primary school level. And it's true that in arithmetic, there are many, many, many questions for which there is one specific acceptable answer. Some educators have suggested that offering problems that have multiple solutions to pupils can provide some useful alternatives to right/wrong logic. For example, if pupils are asked to find the product of 12 and 14, they might use long multiplication; they might build on the fact that they know what 12 x 12 is and then add another 12 x 2; or they might break the product up into easier ones, such as 10 x 14 added to 2 x 14. These different strategies, which can vary according to pupils' strengths and experience, can help pupils see that there are many ways of thinking about a problem. This might feel less alienating than the idea of following one definite method. Further, a simple shift in questioning, from 'what is 12 x 14?' to 'how do you work out 12 x 14?' changes the problem from one with a single correct answer, to one in which there are multiple methods that will work.

Shifting the question is one effective strategy for reducing the pressure of right/wrong thinking. Another is to work towards listening *with*, rather than listening *for*. In listening *for*, a teacher is expecting a certain response from the student, which the student's response either meets or does not meet. From the pupils' point of view this can often feel like they're being asked to guess what the teacher is thinking. This does not invite reasoning. So, if the response to the question 'What is 28 x 28?' is '56', and the teacher is listening *for* '784', then the teacher will provide an evaluative response: 'That is incorrect'.

In contrast, listening *with* attempts to construct a logic that fits the response. In this case, the teacher might say, '56 is indeed the sum of 28 and 28.' This form of interaction fits well with the golden rule of improvisation, which is summarised as 'yes, and ...'. If you are improvising in pairs, and your partner says something, you cannot say 'no' or 'that's wrong' or 'you should have done it differently'. Instead, you must play along, fold in what has been done – listen *with* – and co-respond.

Listening *with* is not about avoiding telling pupils they've made a mistake. Instead, it's about helping pupils appreciate the conditions under which their thinking is valid and providing feedback that can direct them towards a valid response to the original question. It's not always easy to figure out what these conditions might be. For example, if the initial response had been 464, the teacher might require some more information from the pupil about how they arrived at the response. In this case, decomposing the product into the sum of two products 20 x 20 and 8 x 8 would not be an uncommon strategy. Instead of saying 'you can't do that with multiplication', listening *with* might involve co-responding with, 'that would be the case if you were finding the area of the shaded parts of this square' (as in the figure below: what products go in the unshaded rectangles?).

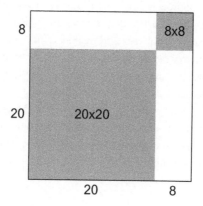

Another way of co-responding in this case, assuming that pupils are quite comfortable with products of numbers less than 10, might be to say 'if 28 x 28 = 464, then 11 x 11 = 101' (if we are thinking of 11 as 10+1). Instead of finding the question that matches with the pupil's response, this brings the logic of the pupil's response into a situation that's more familiar to them. This helps them become aware of the fact that, in some sense, they already *know* that decomposing the factors of a product like 11 x 11 into the sum of 10 x 10 + 1 x 1 does not work.

In this practice of listening *with*, we're intentionally moving away from the language of misconception and mistakes that's often used to describe students' unexpected responses. As other scholars have argued, the problem with the language of misconception is that it does not adequately acknowledge the effective habits and strategies pupils have used to solve other problems, which can lead teachers to want to *replace* erroneous responses with correct ones. This can sometimes work, at least on the surface, at the moment of intervention. In listening *with*, we focus on how the question *and* the response modulate each other, thereby bringing out the habits and assumptions students have successfully used in the past while helping them appreciate the new circumstances they're now working under. Indeed, in the 28 x 28 = 464 case, finding the two products can indeed be part of a productive solution.

From arithmetic to geometry

Another fruitful approach that doesn't involve right/wrong logic is to focus on the geometry part of the curriculum, which is often left to the end of the primary school year and treated as 'fun', in contrast to 'hard' arithmetic. Geometry *can* be fun, of course, but it can introduce students to ways of thinking that support their arithmetic learning *and* expose them to how facts and assumptions are linked.

Of course, there are many 'facts' in geometry. For example, it's a fact that the English word for a polygon with three sides is a triangle. But learning the names of shapes isn't the same thing as doing geometry. Imagine showing a group of Year 2 pupils the shape in the figure below.

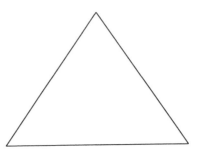

Most of them will quickly say it's a triangle, having seen triangles outside of school. But knowing the name of the shape is not doing geometry. You might show them this second image.

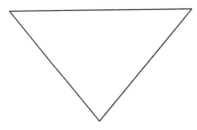

Many pupils will say that the new shape is an upside-down triangle: not a triangle, but an upside-down triangle. They might offer that, in order to be a real triangle, it has to be right-side up. In other words, they want the triangle to *look* like the first image – to have the same orientation as the first basic shape they saw. Now geometry can begin because you can ask, 'Well, what is a real triangle then?' And someone might say, 'It has three sides that are connected', which is a perfectly good description of the first image, as well as the second. If you point that out, some pupils might accept – perhaps even grudgingly – that the second image is indeed a triangle (though they might continue to prefer the first image over the second one!). But once the seed has been sown, the geometric thinking can continue. Show them this third image.

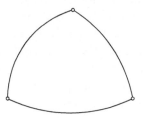

Most pupils won't want to accept it as a triangle, which means that perhaps the proposed definition needs to be modified to something like 'It has three sides connected by straight lines'. Show them another image.

Some students might say it's not a triangle at all, but a stick. But somebody will note that it still has three straight-line sides that are connected. The exploration can continue with different triangles, with examples that pupils have never seen in their daily lives before. This might be a slow process, because it involves the pupils learning to call very different-looking things by the same name which, according to the French mathematician Henri Poincaré, is the very essence of mathematics. But we can go further yet. What happens if the triangle becomes so flat that one of the vertices coincides with the opposite segment? Is *this* still a triangle?

Some students will vehemently oppose this idea. Others might be willing to consider it. A few might propose some reasons, one way or another. If the vertex is right on the opposite side, then the shape has no inside, so it can't be a triangle. Somebody else might say that it is a triangle if you imagine looking at it from a side view, rather than from above. Another student might express some flexibility, noting that it still has three vertices and three sides, but it just so happens that they are overlapping.

The point we are trying to make here is that we are no longer in the realm of right/wrong, because it depends how we want to define the word 'triangle'. It may be that it is decided, as a class, that a triangle has three straight sides that are connected, but not overlapping. In other words, the point is to work through the images and the words together in order to agree a definition. This is less about right/wrong than about coming up with a wide variety of examples of a given shape, as well as some reasons for why certain examples should be included or not. This sort of experience can help students see that definitions do not come pre-made from heaven; they are negotiated explorations.

Geometry can be an especially fertile terrain for working through definitions in this way, particularly because it often involves an interplay between language and diagrams. Since diagrams are always particular (one specific triangle or another), they can easily hide some generalisations. For example, in the first triangle shown on page 38, even though we know it's only one specific triangle, it can easily be seen as a template of a triangle, which can encourage students to generalise that triangles always have to be 'right side up' or that one side of the triangle must always be horizontal.

Engaging in geometry can also be an effective way to invite different ways of thinking – particularly visual and dynamic ones – into the classroom, while making quick and numerical ways of thinking less dominant than usual. This will help children appreciate that different people can be 'good' at maths in different ways. This is not just true in the classroom, but also amongst professional mathematicians. Some prefer more geometric approaches, looking for analogies or connections between ideas; others prefer precise, analytical approaches. Both are required for the field to advance.

Moreover, since mathematics itself is pluralist – there are many ways of thinking about any concept – there can always be more geometrical or more dynamic approaches. Above, we offered a more geometrical way of thinking about 28 x 28, for example. But even addition and subtraction can be thought of in geometric terms through the idea of the number line, which gives a visual image of how different numbers relate to each other, and how operations work. For example, when you think of 13 − 24, you might think of it in purely numerical terms, perhaps breaking up 24 into 13 + 11 in order to find the difference. But many people imagine a number line with a point at 13 and a series of 24 hops going backwards towards 0 and beyond. The number line provides a way of visualising position and a tool for operating − in this case for subtracting. Subtracting becomes a dynamic process of hopping along the line towards the left, whereas adding is about hopping towards the right.

Within the research literature, it's becoming clear that spatial reasoning is a very important aspect of mathematical thinking, even in contexts that have little to do with geometry. Spatial reasoning involves picturing objects in your mind, moving them around and moving yourself around. For example, you might imagine a number line and a person standing on the number line, then moving forward along it. You might also picture being on the number line yourself, watching the person move away from you. Children who are successful at spatial reasoning tend to outperform their peers. Since spatial reasoning is flexible, we have many potential opportunities as teachers to help our students practise and improve their spatial reasoning. This can involve asking them to *imagine* hopping on a line, or inviting them to *draw* their own number line and use it to model an arithmetic operation, or challenging them to *describe* what their number line would look like if it was extended in both directions or if they zoomed in to see what lies between 1 and 2. These are exercises that are much less about being right or wrong than about developing mental powers that help to provide meaning and confidence.

Throughout this chapter, we've been trying to shift away from a right/wrong binary entirely focused on the answer towards a relational view. The relational view involves a focus on the contingency of a solution: how an answer may be correct given certain assumptions or how it aligns with certain questions. This can also extend to ways of thinking about the question and, in particular, the possibility of thinking with images and visual models. Here we're less concerned with the answer than we are with the tools that can be used to think through a problem. You'll know you have succeeded in shifting students' attention to more productive ways of thinking when they ask you, 'Is there a visual way of thinking about this?'!

Putting into practice B: Symbolically structured environments

Engaging pupils in mathematical problem-solving can be really valuable. These problems are often more complex than textbook exercises, and sometimes require methods that haven't been explicitly taught. A problem-solving environment (PSE) is one where pupils are given challenging problems they can't solve by applying methods they already know. In this chapter, we'll be introducing symbolically structured environments (SSEs), where pupils are given a set of mathematical rules and asked to use these rules to find new patterns.

Here's an analogy that illustrates some of the differences between PSEs and SSEs. A PSE is like a tennis match. There is one player playing against another, with a net dividing their two sides. When one player sends the ball to the other side of the court, the other player either hits it back into the other player's side of the court or misses. Depending on the location of the tennis court, the ball can sometimes be sent far away, sometimes over the fence surrounding outdoor courts. A squash game is more like an SSE. When one player hits the ball after the serve, it must first touch the front wall, but it can then bounce against the other walls between certain lines before being hit by the other player. The ball stays within the limits of the court, and the ball can't go far when a player fails to hit it.

By returning to the idea of listening *for* and listening *with*, we can see that in the former, the pupil response is like the tennis ball that is either hit within the court or not – it's either right or not. But for squash, the ball can hit several different walls, each one contributing to its journey – there's bounce, ricochet, change in direction; the other player must listen with the ball *and* the wall.

We see a symbolically structured environment as being like a squash court because it is a constrained area in which a significant amount of feedback is given, not just by the other player, but mainly by the walls and floor – the maths itself talks back. As the mathematician Francis Su (2020) writes, this action-reaction phenomenon occurs in many forms of play, like in jazz, when one instrument responds to another. We set this in relation to many problem-solving environments, which are more like tennis courts, in the sense that the problem is either solved or not; the teacher is often the only feedback mechanism provided and this can mean that solutions can sometimes exceed the limits of the court.

Of course, both tennis and squash are wonderful games. We are not setting up a new binary in order to privilege one game over another. Instead, we use an analogical method to help highlight how symbolically structured environments (SSEs) might feel and work differently, particularly in ways that can sustain the contingency of mathematical assertions and actions. In SSEs, the walls are more like mathematical structures that respond through symbols of one kind or another. Many actions are possible within the SSE, and almost any action can be met with a reaction that provides feedback on the system as a whole.

First, we'll outline the specific features of working within SSEs that are relevant to the dogma that 'Maths is always right or wrong'. The first feature is that SSEs allow us to focus on how a question fits an answer, or how a generalisation fits an assumption, instead of only whether a child's answer is right or wrong. We see this as a relational view of maths. The second is that SSEs allow the questioning and thought to come from all pupils, as well as *from the mathematics itself*, instead of the normal method of the lesson being led by the teacher as the authority figure. Here's an example.

Pick's Theorem

The teacher draws two shapes on a dot grid (perhaps by projecting a screen), as shown opposite and says: 'These are both 8-dot shapes.'

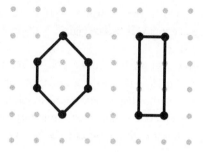

The teacher continues, saying, 'Someone come and draw a different 8-dot shape.' Students come to the board and, without explaining why, the teacher indicates if each shape is 8-dot or not.

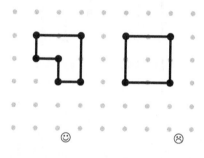

The aim is for students to notice that the shapes are labelled by adding up the number of dots both inside the shape and on the perimeter. Rather than trying to explain this, which might lead to confusion, the teacher invites pupils to do it for themselves. The teacher can't know what pupils will draw, but gives feedback each time. The teacher continues inviting pupils to draw new shapes until they are able to explain what makes a shape an '8-dot shape'. The right-hand shape in the figure above is classified as '9-dot'.

Pick's Theorem is used to determine the area of a polygon drawn on a square dot grid. It connects three features polygons have. Pupils can work with multiple relationships: for example, by fixing one feature and varying the other two. The theorem states that, if A is the area of the shape, I is the number of dots on the inside and B is the number of dots on the border, then $A = B/2 + I - 1$.

An entry into work on the theorem is described in the seminal book *Starting Points* by Banwell, Saunders and Tahta (1986). Here's an example of how it can be used in the classroom. This is reconstructed from a lesson that took place in a Year 8 class (ages 12–13) in an English school where Alf used to work.

The teacher now asks pupils to draw a shape and then write I (for the number of dots 'inside'), B (for the number of dots on the 'border') and A (for the area of the shape) next to it. Pupils will have met the concept of 'area' before, but might need reminding about it. The class works together, finding the three values (I, B, A) for each of the shapes on the board.

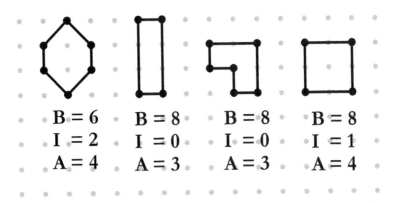

This activity works as an SSE for several reasons. First, note that the symbols offered are B, I and A. There are many things that could have been explored about the shapes, but the teacher has offered these as 'walls' as a way of enclosing the space while still providing sufficient room for action and thought. Now, with any shape that a student draws, they can determine the values of B, I and A. The shape itself asserts the values, not the teacher. The situation is fertile because there are many conjectures that can be made about those symbols.

Having collected all the information, the teacher says: 'OK, look at all the shapes we have drawn here, what do you notice? What's the same? What's different? Can anyone make a prediction? Or ask a question?'

Jordan: They all have straight lines.

Teacher: Nice, and that is one of the rules for this task – all the shapes you draw must have straight lines.

Alice:	The area is 3 or 4.
Teacher:	Right, for all the shapes we have here, the area is 3 or 4. So, could someone turn that into a question or a challenge?
Mike:	Are the areas always 3 or 4?
Teacher:	Lovely, so let's have that as a challenge – can you find an 8-dot shape where the area is not 3 or 4? (*writing this on the board*)
Abi:	If the inside is zero, the area is 3.
Teacher:	So, we have our first conjecture on this project. Abi, can you say that again and I am going to write it down, and remember this is just for 8-dot shapes that we are looking at.
	Abi repeats this and the teacher writes it on the board:
	Abi's conjecture: for 8-dot shapes if $I = 0$, then $A = 3$.
Teacher:	So, how could we test Abi's conjecture?

The teacher can't know what the pupils will notice and therefore must listen *with* rather than listen *for*. Some things the pupils say will allow tasks to be set up for the class, related to the problem. It doesn't really matter what is said, so long as it can lead to questions, challenges or conjectures. In other words, the ball can hit any wall, and a rebound can be produced. The teacher is alert to how pupils' statements could become things for others to work on (for example, with Alice's and Abi's comments above).

Linking pupils' names to their conjectures highlights the idea that conjectures arise from observation and action, and are not *only* made by famous or talented mathematicians. At this stage in the lesson, you could set up some independent or paired work. Plan in times for the class to regroup to discuss what they have noticed. During this first phase of independent work, you could set up a way of collecting results, as in the table on page 48. Pupils come up to the board to add to it whenever they find a new shape. The structure of the table invites questions such as, 'What is the greatest number of dots you can have inside an 8-dot shape?' Along the way, a shared definition of what an 8-dot shape is can be agreed, with the range of examples making it easier for pupils to see what the shared characteristics are. Once an 8-dot shape has been defined, the 9-dot shape will seem easy to identify and create.

8-dot shapes		
B	**I**	**A**
8	0	3
6	2	4
8	0	3
7	1	3.5

As you may have noticed, there were several mathematical content connections offered here, including:

- distinguishing area from perimeter, finding the areas of shapes without counting squares, finding the areas of triangles as half of a rectangle and finding the areas of compound complex shapes;
- opportunities for mathematical thinking;
- making predictions about the areas of '8-dot shapes', '9-dot shapes' and so on, making conjectures, testing conjectures, finding counterexamples, expressing conjectures using algebra, finding relationships between three variables.

Now we can go through our tennis-squash/PSE-SSE analogy more thoroughly - there are several key features to note. In a PSE, there is often one problem to be solved, whereas in an SSE, the problem emerges out of a set of actions. Likewise in tennis, there is one direction for the ball to go, over the net, whereas in squash, the ball might bounce off several walls, changing direction as it moves. In a PSE, there is little feedback given – whether or not the solution is correct is often determined externally, whereas in an SSE, feedback is given from actions in relation to mathematical symbols. Likewise in tennis, there are no walls for the ball to bounce off, unless it goes astray, whereas in squash, the closed-in court encourages bounce – moreover, the movement of the ball is contingent on the relation of wall and ball.

On symbolically structured environments

In a sense, maths itself is a structure with defined symbols and constraints. However, it can still produce new and unexpected things. That's why mathematicians are still making discoveries! In the same way, for Pick's Theorem, pupils might come up with a range of conjectures – what matters is that they emerge from the constraints of the 'game'. SSEs are both constrained by mathematical rules and open to new patterns. Here are some features of SSEs:

1. Symbols stand for actions or distinctions – they tell you what to do or look for. In our example, the labels of I and B are used to tell pupils to count dots (on the inside or along the border) and look for differences across shapes.

2. Symbol use is governed by mathematical constraints embedded in the structuring of the environment. This means that rules for symbol use do not need to be memorised, but can be enacted and corrected, if needed, using the feedback from the SSE. In our example, one constraint is that the shapes are on a square dot grid, which ensures that there are relationships to be found between the three values I, B and A.

3. Symbols can be immediately linked to their inverse. They are not taught in isolation. In our example, as a result of putting results in tables, pupils move from finding the area of shapes to the inverse challenge of looking for shapes that have given areas (in order to fill in missing rows of the table).

4. Complexity can be constrained. There are rules, but still lots of freedom. In our example, the teacher constrains attention to only 8-dot shapes initially, before opening up the space to other numbers of dots (but still constrains students to focus on a specific number at a time).

5. Novel symbolic moves can be made. In our example, new symbolic relationships are noticed by the students; the actual shape of the 8-dot polygons can vary enormously (common polygons, concave ones, etc.).

In an SSE, the teacher focus is not on whether the pupils' maths is right or wrong. While pupils are energised by patterns they notice, the teacher's attention is on whether their ideas can be turned into a question or conjecture that others could use to guide their work. While pupils are engaged with their own sense of what an 8-dot polygon is, the teacher's attention is on the talk taking place and whether students are reasoning and hearing the reasoning of others.

This focus requires the teacher to listen *with* the detail and subtlety of student contributions. In our examples, the teacher is not listening out *for* particular responses (in the sense of a 'right' answer), but for particular kinds of example (the right 'kind' of answer). It's important to be familiar with the environment, so you can focus on the kinds of things pupils say, without worrying about what might happen next. There's a paradox here. It is hard to work within an SSE that is new to you. And yet, the only way to become more comfortable teaching within such an environment is to use it. The teacher in our example was experienced at working within this type of environment, and could comfortably take on the role of orchestrating events, rather than directing them (for example, judging when to move students on to looking at other dot shapes).

It's important to note that in the SSE we described, there are situations in which right/wrong judgements are appropriate, as well as situations when contingent thinking is more valuable. For example, the teacher needed to tell which shapes qualified as 8-dot shapes, as the 8-dot shape was one the teacher introduced and there was no way for the student to figure out its meaning. In Hewitt's (1999) language, the 8-dot shape is part of what can be considered arbitrary mathematics, because it could have been defined in a different way. This does not mean that the teacher begins with a definition, since it's often the case that the best way to come to know something is to see many different examples of it, as with the triangle discussion in Dogma B. In the case of Pick's Theorem, the teacher offered just enough evaluative feedback to get the game going. Afterwards, the feedback was coming from the mathematics, with the teacher providing the symbols and the table, helping to articulate pupils' ideas, and prompting their thinking about counterexamples.

Summary

We both work with university graduates wanting to be maths teachers. The most common thing these graduates say about why they enjoyed maths at school is that they did so because it was either right or wrong. They often contrast this black and white nature with studying literature, where they sometimes express frustration at there never being 'correct' answers. The dogma that 'Maths is always right or wrong' is perhaps one of the most strongly held, or at least the most frequently expressed, of the five dogmas in this book. The contrast with literature is an interesting one, because of course there are black and white questions you can ask about literature, such as: 'What is the name of Hamlet's father?' or 'What are the first lines of Hamlet?' or 'How many acts are there in Hamlet?' But in literature lessons, teachers tend not to be too interested in those kinds of question; instead plays and novels and poems are used to raise questions about human nature, about the characters' motivations, about the effect of the writing on the reader. This is remarkably similar to studying maths – there are a range of different kinds of questions that can be asked in any context, some of which have straightforward answers (such as 'What is the area of this shape?') and some of which don't (such as 'What patterns do you notice?'). The difference is that maths teachers have tended to value the black and white questions in studying maths, rather than the more interesting, nuanced and subtle ones, which do not have straightforward answers.

As discussed in the previous chapter, mathematical truths are entirely linked to the starting points or assumptions they are based on. In other words, no truth is absolute and a truth in one system can be contrasted with a different truth in another system. We proposed the value of developing *spatial reasoning* with children, as a way to engage the imagination and as a way to support children in being producers of mathematics (only they can say what they have imagined). In this chapter, we offered the classroom example of working in a symbolically structured environment as one where children can experience some of the constraints of mathematics. SSEs are, for us, the equivalent of a novel or play – a space within which teachers and students can dwell, asking questions and listening to each other. There will be things that are right or wrong in an SSE, and also opportunities for working on questions which are new, where no one knows what will be found. And while some children may enjoy maths always being right or wrong, we know there are many more who are turned off by this, perhaps sensing that in real life things aren't always so easy.

Dogma C:
'Maths is culture-free'

Nathalie's story

A few years ago, I was working with some Elders from the Nuu-chuh-nulth First Nation (located on Vancouver Island, in British Columbia) on translating numbers into their language, for the *TouchCounts* iPad application. This was not an easy task because the Nuu-chuh-nulth people were forced to give up speaking their language in the residential schools set up by the government of Canada, which means there are now very few fluent speakers left. Also, there are variations in the language that depend on specific geographical locations—those who lived on the ocean used numbers differently from those who lived on the river. This meant that some of the larger numbers, like 60, are said differently by different Elders.

I was intrigued by the different meanings that the number names have. For example, the word for 'nine', *cả waakwał*, means one less than ten. I was asking the Elder whether the word 'seven' – which is *ʔaƛpu* – had any particular meaning. The Elder started making a pinching gesture with her thumb and index finger, and mentioned plucking the feathers of a chicken. I was astounded, finding it hard to believe that chickens and seven had anything in common. She then started counting, from 1 to 10, both out loud and with her fingers. And all of a sudden, it all made sense. The gesture accompanying *ʔaƛa* (two) was a pinching gesture on her right hand and the gesture accompanying *ʔaƛpu* was the same pinching gesture on the left hand. In Nuu-chuh-nulth, the numbers 2 and 7 have a symmetry that is completely missing in the English language. And their accompanying gestures are inextricably linked with a specific cultural practice. (Also, the gesture for four, *muu*, is like a V, but with the index and middle fingers extended and held together on one side, and the ring and pinkie fingers extended and held together on the other side, showing as clear as day that 4 is 2 and 2!)

But the story is not over. After the Elder finished counting to ten, she told me that she had not done that since she was eight years old, when she was sent to the residential school. It was an emotional moment. It was also an incredible testament to the strength of the memory of her fingers and to the fact that numbers are much more than symbols, much more than words – they are furled up in our experiences of life, painful as they may be. Numbers are objects we use to count and calculate, but they are also specific ways of moving our bodies.

In elementary classrooms around the world, children learn to read. They learn to read in different languages, using different alphabets or characters (as in Mandarin) or ideographs (as in Ojibwe), and different storybooks. There are some classic children's books that have been translated into many languages, but the staples of a single classroom in one country will be different from those of a classroom in another country. There is a good reason for this: these books reflect local culture, local myths, local experiences, local values. But, in these schools, the mathematics lessons will look very similar – in most (but not all) countries, studying numbers involves the use of Hindu-Arabic numerals. Everyone begins by learning to count, and then proceeds to arithmetic operations. Mathematics seems somewhat universal in this regard, much less inflected by local cultures and values.

And then there is the fact that anywhere you go, 2 + 2 = 4. There's a kind of universal agreement about this and many other mathematical 'facts', which suggests that maths is not about opinions or fads, that it stays the same whether you live in a democratic country or a dictatorship; whether you are religious or not; whether you are male or female or non-binary or gender-fluid; whether you belong to the working or the upper class. Indeed, if maths has this kind of universality, it is in part because of the need to trade and communicate across peoples and cultures.

Mathematics includes language, bodies and land

Alongside being universal, maths is also very local, as Nathalie's story illustrates. This is because maths is done by humans, and humans are shaped by their various and intersecting relations with each other, with the land on which they live and with their histories. For example, it's common across almost all cultures that people use their hands to count. In each of these cultures, they do so differently. Sometimes the differences are small: in England, counting often begins by extending first the thumb, and then each of the fingers in order; in Iran, you start with the pinkie and work through the fingers until the thumb. Sometimes the differences are a little bigger: in India, 'seven' might involve extending the thumb of the right hand and the thumb and index of the left hand (the fingers of the right hand each standing for 5); in Papua New Guinea, it involves touching the arm, halfway between the wrist and the elbow.

Mathematical meanings emerge not just from how we use our hands, but also, and perhaps even more significantly, from how we use our words. Each mathematical word we use has a history and set of meanings. The word 'multiplication' denotes the idea of folding ('ply') many times (multi-). This gives rise to the idea of multiplication being many copies or repetitions of something, as you might get if you fold a piece of paper. In Turkish, multiplication is *çarpma işlemi*. The word *çarpma* is the noun form of the verb *çarpmak* which means 'to hit' or 'to crash'. The word *işlem* means operation, so *çarpma işlemi* literally means the operation of hitting/crashing. The verb and noun are also used to describe situations involving electric shock. The image of multiplication is less about multiple folding than about two quantities 'hitting' each other.

Since 3 x 5 = 15 in both 'multiplication' and *çarpma işlemi*, it's tempting to say they're the same. But it's quite hard to figure out how these two ways of thinking can give the same answer, or can even refer to the same thing! We can therefore say that there's agreement on the fact that 3 x 5 = 15, but not necessarily on how or why it does. In other words, there's something about maths that's both universal *and* local. One thing that's emerged from international studies in maths education is that certain ways of thinking in one culture might help learners in a different culture.

But the mixing of mathematical ways of thinking across cultures is very old. The history of the 'Hindu-Arabic' numerals, which is anything but culture-free, shows this clearly. It's a long and complicated story of indirect transmission from Indian to Arabic to European people. Indian people were the first to use one single symbol for each of the first ten numbers, dating back to the third century BCE. These 'Brahmi' numbers morphed into Gupta numerals (fourth to the sixth century) and then the Nagari numbers (seventh to the eleventh century), which were transmitted into the Arab world, and then into the European world.[1] These numerals resemble more closely our current ones.

[1] The Mayans also used the Gods for their number names (including a zero) at around the same time, in 4CE.

In geometry, we can see other traces of our mixed heritage. We use the number 'five', 'fifteen' and 'fifty' from the Germanic *fif*, but we call, for example, five-sided polygons 'pentagons', which uses the Greek root *penta* (-*gon* is angle). At the same time, we use the Germanic 'four' for the number, but the Latin *quadri* to speak of four-sided polygons, quadrilaterals (they could have been called tesseralaterals or even quadrigons!). What we can see in this mixing and matching of words from different languages is the trace of human, cultural and local mathematical meanings. Covering some of these meanings doesn't only invite learners into the non-universal world of mathematics, but also allows students to create new relations with these words and their associated shapes.

The history of measurement provides an extraordinary example of the way mathematics overlaps with culture. With its focus on measuring things in the world – heights of people, weights of liquids, angles of turns, degrees of heat, etc. – measurement epitomises the back-and-forth dance between the local space and context and the more global desires for standardisation. Every culture in the world has developed units of measure, often based on body parts (feet, arm lengths, hand widths), but also on objects (bows, chain links, sticks, poppyseeds). In English, the more frequent source of length units is the human body. Early North American Ojibwe measured how much of a day it would take to travel a certain distance by superimposing an outstretched hand on the arc of the sun: in this analogical measuring, 'one "hand stretch" was considered one fourth of the arc from sunrise to zenith' (Cooperrider & Gentner, 2019, p. 5). Distance can be measured in terms of a 'bow shot' (used in the Andaman Islands), a 'stone's throw' (used in Morocco), the audibility of a human voice (used in Myanmar), or the number of coffee stops required to complete a trip (used by the Sammi).

The use of measures not directly related to the body or to objects emerged later in time, often with much political and conceptual struggle. When the metre was first suggested in 1793, it was revolutionary for being derived from nature itself, since it was defined as being one millionth of the distance from the equator to the North Pole. The metre was celebrated as being egalitarian, since the earth belongs to everyone, which wasn't the case for the units that had been used before. It was first represented as a brass bar marked out with decimal, graduated divisions. The official platinum bar, which was kept in a safe in Paris, had no divisions and in its gleaming perfection, can seem quite removed from any idea of nature – it can serve an ideology of a pure, simple, universal and self-sufficient unit. Eventually, the brass bar was deemed insufficiently precise, as well as prone to change over time. The metre is now defined in relation to the speed of light. Defining it in relation to light might make the unit seem self-sufficient, but it is inevitably bound up with the earth.

Culture isn't restricted to language and land, but can also extend to modes of living such as urban versus rural, or middle class versus working class. Assuming there's no connection is to subscribe to the dogma that maths is culture-free. A culture-free maths could be imagined in the figure below, on the left, which adopts a strict inside/outside separation. The inside represents the core, objective mathematical ideas. It doesn't change. It might have outside layers, like language, history and technology which depend on culture and context, but they don't affect what's on the inside. We might be aware of the fact that children from lower-income families struggle more with maths than those from upper-income families; a culture-free view of mathematics assumes that this is explained by factors such as a lack of parental support or insufficient food, shelter or resources. But this assumption separates maths from culture – assuming that there's nothing about maths itself that makes it more or less infiltrated by middle-class values.

Consider instead the image on the right, in which inside and outside aren't so clearly defined, but spread across a continuum instead. There might be some moments when everyone agrees on some meanings and truths, but there may also be variations of interpretations, local truths and contingent facts.

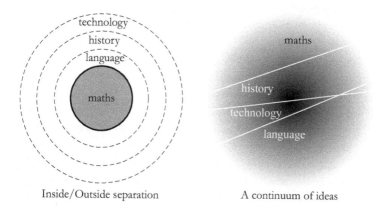

Inside/Outside separation   A continuum of ideas

Nathalie's story at the beginning of this chapter illustrates well the way in which maths can't be separated from historical, linguistic and technological dimensions. The Elder's technology of counting is almost universally shared amongst humans, but her particular way of doing so is quite culturally specific.

The image on the right is also a way to make sense of Valerie Walkerdine's research, which focuses specifically on class (e.g. Walkerdine, 1990). She documents the kinds of conversations that lower-income families might have compared to those of higher-income families. For higher-income families, talking about money can easily become speculative and playful, such as when a parent makes a game out of calculating the change that will be given at a café: 'What if I bought …?' For lower-income families, you might have a discussion about what can be afforded – perhaps a parent convincing their child to have something less expensive. Even if they're doing very similar calculations – even if the calculations are identical – the maths in one case is a matter of survival while in the other, it's a matter of exercising what Walkerdine calls 'symbolic control'. She provides another example of class difference relevant to maths learning, describing a group of seven-year-olds playing a shopping game in which they're given cards to buy certain products. While children from higher-income homes pay little attention to the actual costs – perhaps ignoring the game context to focus only on the numbers – the children from lower-income families paid more attention to the nonsensical prices these items cost and imagined the people they would have to become in order to purchase them in real life, thereby paying little attention to computation.

These kinds of tensions have become more pressing now that the importance of culturally relevant pedagogies is recognised. Once you're aware of cultural assumptions, it can be surprising just how frequently they come up in textbook maths problems. There might be cricket contexts – how many children will understand this? What about a gardening context or eating sushi or buying large packs of bottled drinks at a supermarket? One option is to spend time to explain the context. An alternative is to resort to safe, widely shared experiences, like sleeping or being in a classroom. In homogeneous classrooms, where many pupils share similar experiences, it can be hard to notice the cultural assumptions being made. One attraction for us of symbolically structured environments (SSEs), discussed in Putting into practice B, is that the context of an SSE can be purely mathematical.

Mathematics culture and values

Culturally relevant mathematics does not just involve choosing situations that are relevant to specific cultures, like a football problem in England and an ice hockey one in Canada. Culture isn't just about activities or food or language, but also about values. And, believe it or not, even maths is shaped by values. Many people find this hard to believe. But in his study of Western mathematics, Alan Bishop (Bishop, 1988) has identified three pairs of values that have shaped the discipline: two ideological values (rationalism and objectivism); two sentimental values (control and progress); and two sociological values (openness and mystery). The ideological values are about what is seen to count as true or real, and can be thought of as beliefs about knowledge. The sentimental ones are beliefs about humanity's future. And the sociological ones are beliefs about humanity's relationship to mathematics.

Because these are values, it means that they can change over time and that they can look different in other cultural practices. It also means that they can change. Furthermore, it means that when you teach maths, you are also teaching a set of values, even if you aren't consciously aware of it. In fact, sometimes these values seem so 'natural' that we don't realise they represent the preferences and desires of mathematicians, rather than necessary aspects of maths. We first want to draw attention to these values, so that you can better understand the preferences they involve. But we also want to stress that the values that have shaped Western mathematics do not necessarily need to be adopted in the maths classroom. Therefore, we hope that once we have covered these maths values, you can make choices about the values you want in your teaching.

Let's begin with the first pair of values. The ideological value of rationalism is committed to deductive or logical reasoning as the preferred way of achieving explanations and conclusions. If you read a mathematical proof, you will see a sequence of arguments, each one depending on the truth of the previous steps, connected by logical inferences. This is the public, official story about mathematics. In actual lived experience, however, mathematicians make guesses, they use their intuition, they draw pictures, they try to get a feel for ideas, they follow paths that seem more beautiful or familiar, and they generally meander their way towards solving problems.

As a maths teacher, you can help pupils to see when these different values are appropriate. If pupils are just starting to work on a problem, you might value a tentative explanation that is open to being questioned, even if it's just a guess. For example, if asked whether 6 is even or odd, a pupil might just guess at the answer. It's a starting point. As pupils are sharing their ideas, you might value respect – listening to one's classmates – and humility. If one pupil says that 6 is even because it can be divided into two equal groups, then you might value the way another pupil restates that idea in their own words. You might value another way of explaining why 6 is even. And if a pupil says that 6 is not even, you might value this contribution because it can encourage their classmates to find more convincing arguments. All of these values can sit alongside the valuing of logical reasoning. What is important is to make your values clear to pupils.

The ideological partner of rationalism is objectivism, in which ideas can be given objective meanings, thereby enabling them to be dealt with *as if* they had an objective reality that was independent of human interpretation. This means that numbers, points, fractions, functions, etc. are treated as objects that have specific attributes, just like an apple and a tree do, that everyone can see. This value of objectivism leads to a certain way of speaking about mathematics, like 'a square has four sides' or 'an even number is divisible by 2' in which the human is absent. We don't typically say, for example, 'when I count the sides of this square, I count up to 4', which would emphasise a particular person counting and a particular square. Again, like the value of rationalism, it turns out that objectivism may not always be appropriate. Even in mathematics, there's lots of evidence that mathematicians personalise mathematical objects when they are working on problems.

Indeed, many educators have talked about the importance of humanising mathematics, of helping them see that maths is something that humans do, and therefore maths involves feelings, experiences, history, beliefs, desires and so on. For example, pupils are often taught the names of different polyhedra, such as 'cube' or 'tetrahedron', as if these objects have always existed. But in fact, the concept of a polyhedron only emerged out of a long process involving the study of three-dimensional shapes. Mathematicians were interested in a particular relation that seemed to hold for many of them, which is the relationship between the faces, sides and vertices. For a cube and for a pyramid, $V-E+F=2$, but the relationship doesn't hold for the double-pyramid shown below on the right. As it turns out, the name polyhedron is only given to only those three-dimensional shapes that satisfy the relationship V−E+F=2. And since mathematicians wanted to make sure that common three-dimensional shapes like spheres and cylinders got counted as polyhedra, they found a way to make the relationship work by changing what counts as a vertex, edge and face!

Vertices: 8
Edges: 12
Faces: 6

Vertices: 4
Edges: 6
Faces: 4

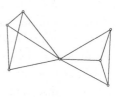

Vertices: 7
Edges: 12
Faces: 8

Nowadays, we just define a polyhedron without going through the whole drama again. This is good for progress, and celebrates the value of objectiveness, but it is not always good for learners, who feel that they are just being handed down truths. As a teacher, you can help pupils appreciate the idea that mathematical objects actually have a history. You can ask: Where did the idea of triangles come from? When would it have been useful? What about the idea of numbers like 2 or 3? Perhaps to compare which of two families had more children? Or to keep track of whose turn it was to be fed? Such discussions do not need to take long, but they can help pupils see how an idea that starts out embedded in a certain practice can eventually develop a life of its own. While the discipline of maths progresses by forgetting this history, the learning of maths is enriched by it.

Bishop's next pair of values are control and progress. The control value is associated with the desire to predict, which in turn is associated with a quest for security and mastery. The very act of predicting what will happen in a sequence of patterns, which is a frequent primary school activity, can provide a sense of control, by making us feel that we know what will come next and even what the 100th design will look like. Algorithms can also provide a sense of control in that they offer a recipe for how to undertake an operation, such as multiplication, no matter what the values of the inputs are. With so much time spent on learning how to use the algorithm, teachers can sometimes forget to help learners appreciate their power. By asking pupils to each write down two numbers that can be multiplied, you could generate a whiteboard filled with unique pairs of numbers such as 13 x 5 or 56 x 93 or 1784726 x 34, and so on – not just the numbers that are given on worksheets. Here the point wouldn't be to find the product, but instead to become more aware of the power of the algorithm.

The control value can also create problems, when mathematical algorithms or formulas are used without taking into consideration the impact they might have on human lives or on the environment. Furthermore, not everything in the world can be controlled. It could help pupils to understand the limits of maths by being exposed to problems that cannot be solved. These can be problems within maths itself. For example, while we have an algorithm that allows us to find the product of any two numbers, the inverse is not true: if you are given a very big number, there is no algorithm for finding its factors (and this is why cryptography works). Maths cannot help you predict what you will get if you toss a coin (though it can help you predict what will happen if you toss 100 coins!). Maths cannot predict whether it will be sunny in two months; it cannot predict whether you will fall in love with someone; whether a meteor might hit. The maths class is a great place to put maths in its place – to highlight its power as well as its limitations.

The progress value, an attitude complementary to control, includes feelings of growth, development, change and the desire to make the unknown known. Progress relates to the 'Maths is a building- block subject' dogma discussed in Dogma A, because things that were unknown before are known now and will remain known in the future. While pupils are unlikely to contribute to the progress of maths in the sense of coming up with new theorems while they are at school, they can certainly contribute to progress within a classroom by developing new ways of understanding or explaining things. The fact that mathematicians spend lots of time coming up with new ways of proving ideas (there are at least 10 different ways of proving the Pythagorean theorem!) shows that progress in mathematics is also about developing new ways of understanding.

For example, you might already know that the sum of two odd numbers is always even. You might know this because you tested many examples. But a different way of understanding might be through a spatial argument, as shown below. While it is specific to the numbers 9 + 7, it also shows how the argument would work for any pair of odd numbers – the two pieces, each with an extra dot, would always 'fit' together. Still a different way would involve using algebra. Since each even number can be written as 2 times n, for any value of n, then the sum of two odd numbers can be written as $2n + 1 + 2m + 1$, which is the same thing as $2(n+m+1)$, which in turn must be an even number. In considering all of these ways of understanding, you are not progressing in terms of accumulated knowledge, but you are progressing in terms of the richness of your knowledge. Any idea you work with in the maths class can be approached through multiple ways of understanding, such as empirical, visual and algebraic. It is worth spending time to expose pupils to these different ways of understanding.

The final set of values proposed by Bishop is that of openness and mystery. Openness is concerned with the fact that, 'Mathematical truths, propositions and ideas generally, are open to examination by all' (p. 75) and that they're therefore seemingly not dependent on opinion, politics, cultural differences or beliefs. Of course, anyone who has opened a mathematics journal published in the past century knows that the mathematics there is hardly open to examination by all. As Bishop points out, one must first know the conventions and symbols being used, and second, find the ideas appealing enough to attempt to make sense of them. Thus, the openness value might better describe the *desire* to achieve universal and 'pure' knowledge which, in principle, can be openly verifiable – independently of psychological or political issues.

In order to be universal, such knowledge – the demonstrations and proofs – must be formalised into declarations that admit no subjective interpretations, and which make ideas explicit and open to criticism and objective analysis. But it is impossible to get rid of all subjectivity. The very idea that there are values in mathematics implies that there are preferences, habits and even fads at play. These have changed dramatically over time, and there is no reason to think they will not continue to change. Openness might involve, in some communities, ways of explaining that are more persuasive or insightful to a greater number of people, which seems to us a reasonable goal in the classroom. Discussing with pupils which explanations or solutions are 'better' for them (Do they prefer the visual argument given above? Are they more convinced by trying lots of examples?) is part of doing mathematics, because it is part of exploring what makes sense – and also, how what makes sense may change over time.

Finally, the mystery value. From a historical point of view, mathematicians have long been associated with astrology, alchemy and magic. And, from a more contemporary point of view, questions such as the following continue to mystify non-mathematicians: What is mathematics? Who does mathematics, why and for what ends? Bishop argues that mathematical mystery originated partly in the ancient Greek cultivation of exclusiveness. Mathematicians took steps to preserve their mystery by making mathematics that was abstract and removed from everyday life. The Pythagorean pledge of secrecy can be seen as a quest for exclusivity in the close connection between mystery and mysticism.

But mystery can also be attractive, and connected to feelings of wonder, surprise and disbelief. Young children often experience wonder around big numbers and the idea of infinity. How is the idea of infinity even possible? This might turn into surprise when they find out that there are different kinds of infinity. Or disbelief when they find out that even though there are infinitely many even numbers (2, 4, 6, 8, 10, 12, …) and infinitely many whole numbers (1, 2, 3, 4, 5, 6, …), the size of those two sets of number is the same. Similarly, children may wonder at the fact that there are four- and even five-dimensional shapes, and be surprised that any quadrilateral can be used to tile a floor and have disbelief at the fact that for some geometers, there is no difference between a doughnut-shaped object and a coffee cup. Experienced as mystery, these ideas can attract students' attention and interest, and help them see that mathematics is not just about memorising facts and formulas, but also about deep, jaw-dropping ideas.

We wanted to highlight the fact that maths is full of values. If maths is assumed to be culture-free, it's because these values are taken for granted, as being just the way maths is. And while it's true that some of these values tend away from the subjective, the affective, the human, it doesn't mean that maths is devoid of subjectivity, emotion and humanity. Furthermore, in the maths classroom, the question of what is valued is an important choice that you yourself can make as a teacher.

On cultural impositions

Maths certainly delights some people, and we certainly hope that children can experience such delight in the classroom, just as they might when reading a book or engaging with a piece of visual art. But if we're going to recognise the cultural aspects of maths, then we also must acknowledge the negative effects some of these can lead to. We mentioned one above, in relation to Valerie Walkerdine's idea of symbolic violence, when students feel literally hit over the head by alienating and debilitating mathematical objects. When formulas are created and used without adequate attention to the context in which they'll be applied, they can cause much harm, as Cathy O'Neil shows in her book *Weapons of Math Destruction* (O'Neil, 2016). She shows how the algorithms used to determine which adverts you see on the internet or which products will be recommended to you when you shop online can adversely affect marginalised people. You could argue that it's not the maths itself that's to blame, but the way it's used. However, when following mathematical values, the aim is to produce equations and relations that are universal and unbiased, but it is this very value that ends up making maths blind to social concerns.

In this light, teaching maths involves an important responsibility, not just to provide pupils with tools they'll need in future, but also to help them understand the limits of these tools. This can be done with a wide variety of mathematical concepts. In teaching division, for example, the mathematical operation involves equal partitioning. So, we can split a set of goods into equal parts. But in some cases, we might want to distribute goods in a way that aligns with goals of equity rather than equality. How might we think of division if we want to distribute goods to people who have varying levels of wealth or property, for example? Another example might be asking why wage increases are always given in percentage terms, and what effect this has on wage disparity, compared with fixed sum increases – percentages are mathematically powerful because they provide a common measure through which to compare, but they can also hide significant details.

Similarly, there are some ways of thinking in maths that prioritise some kinds of understanding above others. For example, the value of objectiveness tends to lead to ways of talking that features the use of nouns over verbs. Nouns are less apt to betray a sense of action. We talk about the sum of two numbers rather than saying that we add one number to another. With a verb, there has to be a person involved in the action, and that in turn implies some subjectivity. In cultures where objectiveness is less valued, maths talk involves more verbs. For example, in the Mi'kmaw people of eastern Canada, the word for straight is *pekaq*, which translates as 'it goes straight' (Lunney Borden, 2011). Instead of thinking of a line as fixed and static, the Mi'kmaw line involves movement from one end to another. It's interesting to learn about the ways in which different cultures think mathematically. But, Lunney Borden also argues that using verbs instead of nouns to describe concepts can actually support many pupils' understanding – not just Mi'kmaw ones. Our dynamic triangle example earlier also showed this. In drawing on all of these different ways of thinking, which you might bring into the classroom or might draw out from your students, it's important to treat these ways of thinking with respect, rather than as being inferior to the typical English or Western way of thinking.

Putting into practice C: Mathematics for real-world contexts

We ended the last chapter with thoughts about the responsibilities of teaching maths:

- to teach children tools but also to reflect on the limits of those tools
- to consider what kinds of understandings and ways of knowing are privileged or not privileged.

One way to think about these responsibilities is through the real-world lens of social and ecological justice: bringing to the classroom questions of which groups in society are marginalised and which aspects of the planet's ecology are destroyed by the use of particular tools and practices that are related in some way or another to mathematics.

Culturally responsive mathematics teaching

One strand of work that has addressed social justice issues in maths education goes under the label Culturally Responsive Mathematics Teaching (CRMT). CRMT seeks to incorporate culture, language and community into maths lessons. Teachers teaching in a culturally responsive manner build bridges between schools and communities and use their knowledge of communities to make learning relevant to pupils' lives. Storybooks and storytelling have emerged as an effective strategy in CRMT. In a review of work done within CRMT (see Abdulrahim & Orosco, 2020), the following characteristics were identified:

- having high expectations of all learners
- supporting pupils in critical thinking (including giving them opportunities to pose problems themselves)
- reflecting on your own beliefs and values as a teacher
- encouraging action on social issues
- developing collaborations between students, teachers and communities.

Reflecting on your own values might also extend to reflecting on the values we assume about mathematics itself, such as the three pairs of values discussed in the previous chapter.

Although these characteristics can provide some useful guidance in CRMT work, an overarching stance of *care* is needed. For example, Anne Watson (2021) describes teacher caring as attending to and listening to students, *being alongside* students, as they learn. Learning key concepts from different cultures is also an act of caring. For instance, a group of researchers based in New Zealand, Averill et al. (2009), report that in Māori culture, 'knowledge is perceived as a taonga (treasure) and gift, and care is taken regarding when and with whom knowledge is shared' (p.162). An awareness of such a view of knowledge would be vital in working with students from the Māori culture. An attitude of care perhaps links to values of openness and mystery about the subject of mathematics itself.

Since teachers draw on the norms of their own culture, they can sometimes forget that many of their students are not aware of these norms. In addition to finding out and learning about other cultures, it is also important in CRMT work to make your own norms explicit. This can involve laying open the rules of the game, of what it means to engage in mathematical dialogue, rules that may otherwise only be apparent to students from socially dominant cultural backgrounds. Norms for talk in maths classrooms can be shared and made explicit and all students expected to participate, for instance, in communal chanting or speaking.

Mathematics teaching and social and ecological justice

The idea of maths for social and ecological justice points to questions about the historical processes of colonisation and marginalisation which have led to inequalities across the world. We've met many teachers who want to use their positions to help teach about justice, peace and sustainability but do not know how to incorporate such issues into maths teaching. They want to support positive action, but aren't sure what this should look like. At the same time, children have been gaining extraordinary attention through climate strikes and marches. In other words, children themselves seem to have a good handle on what positive action looks like. The instances of children bringing successful court cases against oil companies is further evidence of their understanding and power, and are a sign of hope. Stories of hope are surely important, given the anxiety that can be provoked by the uncertainties and disruption of climate change and the ongoing effects of social inequality.

A framework from 2011 suggested three ways of approaching questions of sustainability in the classroom: an accommodation approach; a reformation approach; and a transformation approach (Renert, 2011). This was built on the work of environmental educator Stephen Stirling. In an accommodation approach, sustainability simply serves as a context for fairly standard maths teaching. In a reformation approach, questions beyond maths are considered; for instance, the implications of the data being studied (e.g. looking at the link between income and obesity in the UK). Valuing maths as a tool for control might be present in such an approach. In a transformation approach, lessons are geared towards social action and maths becomes a tool towards this broader aim. (Maths as a tool for social change feels to us outside of Bishop's three pairs of values, rationalism and objectivism; control and progress; openness and mystery.) In this chapter, we offer examples of what each of Renert's approaches might look like in the classroom. They're not meant to be read as a hierarchy – each one is appropriate for different contexts.

Accommodating data

Perhaps the most direct way to teach maths for climate justice is in the context of work on statistics and data handling. While these topics aren't often a significant element of the primary curriculum, work on statistics can provide a context for developing and using other number skills, which also prevents statistics from being seen as an isolated area of maths later on. Textbooks and other resources often use invented data for children to work with. Sometimes, exercises present lists of numbers with no context, simply asking children to find the mean or median or mode, for example. One reason for decontextualising data is that real-world data is often messy and complex. If the aim is to teach children the skill of finding averages, then real data may get in the way of that purpose. 'Cleaning up' data can be time-consuming as well. With that in mind, here's a set of data which could be used to practise statistical skills and which may also provoke some thinking about these skills.

> Climate models predict how much wetter or drier a place will
> be in the future. There are different models made by different
> scientists. Botswana currently averages around 34 mm of rain
> per month. Here are 9 predictions for the change in rainfall in
> Botswana (in mm per month) in the coming years: +17; +13; +6;
> -2; -2; -6; -6; -6; -14.

Using this data, there are a number of possibilities as a teacher (see Coles, Darron & Rolph, 2022). Of course you can invite children to find the mean, median and mode of the data. But the more important question – which is both mathematical *and* political – is how these numbers might help to make predictions about the future. For example, if you were advising farmers in Botswana about future risks, which average would you use? And why? Would you choose the most extreme situation, in order to be able to prepare for the worst possible outcome? Or the middle one, to offer a consensus between the two extremes of the forecasts? What would your message be to farmers about what changes in rainfall to expect and, therefore, what kind of future to prepare for? The climate model data arose out of work Alf did with a scientist, Joseph Darron, who works at the UK Meteorological Office on climate modelling. We have been struck by how 11-year-old children have been able to engage in complex thinking about comparing climate models, thinking that Joseph has, at times, compared favourably to the analyses of climate scientists.

    This data has been tweaked slightly to make the mean value zero, in order to provoke the question of whether there'll be no change in rainfall, even though none of the models actually predict *no* change. Two-thirds of models predict a drier future, so would you advise farmers to prepare for drought? But some models predict a much wetter future, so would you ignore these models or try to prepare for both scenarios? And, of course, the models may not be accurate, i.e. the actual changes might be outside the bounds of what the models predict.

These questions are real ones for climate scientists working with policy makers and politicians. There are no definitive answers and the extent to which you allow debate will be the extent to which an accommodation approach shifts into reformation. The complexity of the message – change is coming, but we do not know what change – is one of the reasons why messages about the climate emergency have taken so long to be heard, and been so hard to hear. One of the ways maths teachers can contribute to public debate is by digging into some of the maths behind the headlines and letting children experience some of the difficulties of prediction.

There's another message here as well. While averages can be thought of as factual, rational and objective, in that they involve a small sequence of simple arithmetic operations, how they are used and by whom is far from being so certain or valid. It's worth encouraging pupils to think not just about the number-crunching part of finding the mean, for example, but also the reason to use the mean and the potential implications of reducing a complex situation into one single number.

There are many sources of climate-related data, such as the Meteorological Office in the UK. It's possible to get historical data from different weather stations, for example, to test the extent of climate change in a particular area.

Reforming number

A group of teachers in the Bristol area in the UK have been exploring a particular form of task designed to support maths learning and to raise important questions around sustainability. The overall structure presents children with a sequence of calculations leading them towards posing a question such as, 'If we continue using oil at the rate we do now, how many more years of oil are left in the currently known reserves around the world?' One teacher, Karl Bushnell (see Bushnell, 2018), has created a sequence in which each step presents children with a calculation out of context and a calculation in the context of the problem. Here's an example inspired by Karl's work, with the context questions in bold.

Write the number 2 million in digits. Write the number 3 billion in digits.

In 2014, BP estimated there were 1,688 billion barrels of oil left in the world. Write this out in digits.

Two quantities are linked in the ratio, 1 : 5 million. Using the same ratio, what is the missing number here, 365 : ?

The total world consumption of oil per day for 2016 was 96 million barrels. How many barrels were consumed during the whole year?

If 3,600,000,000 items are used at a rate of 1,200,000 per day, how many days will they last? [Think about what calculation you would need to do.]

When will the oil run out, if no new oil fields are found and if we keep consuming at 2016 levels?

Is it fair to make these assumptions?

What are the implications of running out of oil?

There's a significant shift from the first to the second question. Children are invited to move from seeing a number as a pure object to seeing it as a number of things. These are quite different ways of thinking. Some Indigenous communities in Canada make a distinction between animate and inanimate objects in terms of how they're numbered, a distinction that's mirrored in the shift between pure and applied contexts. The last two questions are the ones that begin to shift this task towards a reformation approach. Having worked on the arithmetic, children are encouraged to reflect on the meaning and implications of what they have discovered – that is, on the mathematics. Perhaps maths can help us control the situation. Children can consider the actions they could take as a result of what they find. Accommodation and reformation approaches are both possible using this task and the previous one, depending on the extent to which you want your pupils to reflect on the meaning and implications of the calculations they perform.

Transformation approaches

The two classroom tasks above don't explicitly prompt children into action. In a transformational approach, maths comes into play as part of the way to achieve a bigger goal. One example comes from a primary school in Mexico. At this school, teachers have been working with scientists, academic educators and a non-governmental organisation (NGO) in order to innovate the curriculum. The context of this school is important. It sits in the catchment area of the river Atoyac, one of the most polluted rivers in the region. The school is near an industrial site, home to several foreign-owned companies, which were encouraged by government policies to set up factories in the region and provide employment. There are regular illegal outflows of byproducts such as dyes and heavy metals into the river. One result of this is an overpowering smell. Being next to the river makes people's eyes and nostrils prickle. There have been no fish in the river for over 20 years; there aren't even insects living on the river now. The water is an opaque blue-grey. The smell is noticeable as far as 1 km away, in a primary school playground. The river used to be a source of livelihood and ritual for past generations, but it's now a danger to health. Rates of childhood leukaemia and miscarriage are all significantly above national levels and linked directly to the pollution of the river.

The centralised Mexican curriculum makes it hard for teachers to find time to address issues around the river pollution. Indeed, students have to use textbooks (each student in Mexico is given a personal copy to write in) which deal with pollution using the example of air pollution in Mexico City. But recently, the teachers in the school have created a network to help them bring the Atoyac river into the curriculum.

A transformation approach might begin with a real problem facing a community. In the case of the Atoyac region, the teachers' network decided to create a memorial 'museum' to the river, with three 'galleries'. One looks to the past, trying to recapture some of the oral histories of what the river was like when it was in health. A second gallery is focused on the present, on collecting and analysing data on the current state of the river and its impact on health. The very act of collecting data – of choosing what to measure, how and for how long – is itself part of the mathematical activity, as well as the political one. Measuring pollution levels will create very different data from measuring the flow of the river, for example, with the former potentially capable of identifying responsibility.

A third gallery focuses on the future and strategies for bringing the river back to health. This final gallery has the explicit aim of getting children active in campaigning for the rights of the river. It also engages children in acts of speculation. What if the companies left the region – could the river be revitalised? What if different dyes could be created that were not as poisonous? We see these as what-if-not? questions that are mathematical in nature: they involve identifying the variables and connections at play in a system, and investigating how changes in these might affect the system.

Eco-anxiety

One significant consideration, in bringing climate change questions into a classroom context, is the potential for causing anxiety. As teachers, it's important we offer a space for children to discuss their feelings. Actually, the same applies to any context we offer children in the classroom. We need to be aware and sensitive that what might appear as an abstract idea to some (e.g. questions about debt) might be a lived experience for others, potentially bringing up strong emotional reactions. Similarly, while in the West we have often had the luxury in the past of considering questions about climate change in a relatively abstract way, increasingly frequent heatwaves, wildfires and floods have brought the issue closer to our doorstep. Increasingly, children may experience bereavements directly linked to climate change. These are not reasons to avoid the topics, but rather to approach them with awareness of the need to create the space for open dialogue about feelings and emotions that might be stirred.

Summary

In Dogma C, we covered the work of Alan Bishop, who proposed three pairs of values that shaped Western views and practices of mathematics: rationalism and objectivism; control and progress; openness and mystery. Unpacking these values exposed how far maths is from being culture-free and highlighted the subjective and ideological choices that influence both what we think maths is and how it's studied. Raising awareness of these values of the subject maths opens possibilities to think about the values of maths we want to present in teaching or working with others. In a technological society, one of the responsibilities of teaching maths is not just to teach children useful mathematical tools (such as how to calculate profits or welfare payments or interpret data), but also to reflect on the limits of those tools (e.g. who benefits from the use of the tool and who is marginalised?).

In this chapter, we focused on teaching maths for social and ecological justice, and where possible, doing the work of using a mathematical tool and then reflecting on its use. We briefly reviewed research within what is known as Culturally Responsive Mathematics Teaching. We then looked in more detail at work with an ecological focus. We offered three examples of classroom tasks, one looking at climate models, one looking at oil use, and one focused on a community response to river pollution. Children's competence when engaging with complex issues speaks against our next dogma that being a 'maths person' is something limited to the few.

Dogma D: 'Maths is for some people, not others'

Nathalie's story

In my first year of teaching in British Columbia, I had grade 7, 8 and 9 (the equivalent of Years 6, 7 and 8 in England and Wales) pupils all in the same class. Not surprisingly, there were several students, mostly girls, who quickly let me know that they were no good at mathematics. Naturally, I wanted to dispel their beliefs. All year, I tried to help them see that they could be successful at maths. Sometimes this meant explaining things in different ways; sometimes I introduced mathematical ideas that were less about computation, such as the geometry you can do on a sphere; and sometimes I just provided the time and space they needed to think confidently.

At the end of the year, the students were rehearsing for the show they had prepared with their drama teacher. They began to sing and encouraged me to join them. I quickly responded that I was a terrible singer, 'Trust me, you don't want me to join you!' One of the grade 9 students, whose name was Alexandra, looked at me with defiant eyes. 'How could you say that?' she asked. 'You've kept telling me all year that I wasn't allowed to say that about maths, but you can say it about singing?' Well, that hit me hard. I felt that I had really disappointed her. I had been caught not practising what I preached. I had not realised what a responsibility it would be to make demands on my students not only in relation to what they could learn, but also how they should think about themselves.

Our guess would be that, if you went into any primary school staffroom in England, you would hear discussion about the children and maths couched in terms of 'ability'. Phrases such as 'my higher ability children' or 'my highers' and, of course, 'my lowers', are commonplace. Indeed, it can seem as though some children 'get' maths more quickly than others. Some children appear to be good at numbers or immediately catch on to what algebra is about; they seem to be able to retain ideas from one week or term to the next and build a complex network of knowledge – these are the 'highers'. Other children seem to take a while even to realise what numbers are and how they can be manipulated. They might be able to follow instructions in one lesson, only to forget what they have done in the next. Concepts such as fractions seem forever shrouded in mystery – these are the 'lowers'. Such categorisations and such language can become seemingly normal and natural, even. And yet, as we'll be suggesting through this chapter and the next, the dogma that 'Maths is for some people, not others' is perhaps the most dangerous and destructive of the five we discuss in the book.

Of course, the idea of ability doesn't only apply to maths. There's a folk psychology view that humans are born with particular talents, and such views get amplified by stories of child prodigies: 13-year-old children going to university, six-year-old piano virtuosos, teenage Olympians. There's a sense that some are born with particular 'gifts' that the rest of us do not have. Counter-narratives, such as Einstein not doing well at school, seem much less well known and considered. The popular science writer Malcolm Gladwell, from a study of expert craftspeople in a range of disciplines, noted that they'd all practised their chosen skill for around 10,000 hours before becoming expert (Gladwell, 2008). Perhaps the myth of the genius who is born with preternatural gifts is a more comforting illusion than contemplating what each of us could become, if we have the opportunity and the desire. What that kind of story does is set up an implicit binary of nature/gifts versus culture/opportunity, and puts the weight of explanation on just one side.

The idea that we have particular abilities in different spheres of life has a history, one that we trace in the next section. It's worth noting at this stage that the fixation on ability is not a global phenomenon. Research in the 1980s into parental views of children's academic achievements in schools, for instance, indicated a broad pattern of Chinese parents attributing the major cause of low achievement to lack of effort, whereas Caucasian-American parents attributed low achievement to a wider range of factors, including ability and luck. In Norway, from 1978 to

2003, streaming schoolchildren on the basis of marks or 'ability' was forbidden by law.

The rise of 'intelligence' testing

We see current views about ability in several countries as directly linked to the history of intelligence testing over the last 150 years. The discovery of genes and heredity in the nineteenth century led to the concept of 'eugenics', coined by Francis Galton, a cousin of Charles Darwin. Galton adopted the word eugenics from the Greek *eugenes* meaning 'well born', 'of good stock' or 'of good birth'. Galton was interested in how ability and inheritance might be passed down from one generation to the next and, in particular, the influence of race on ability and intelligence. Many universities played a historical role in giving legitimacy to eugenics and, in some cases, this role continued into recent times, for instance, through secret meetings of the 'London Conference on Intelligence', where discussion of eugenics continued until 2015. Ideas of giftedness seem to emphasise the idea that individuals have different levels of natural ability.

Around the same time that the science of heredity was starting out, the systematic study of the human mind ('psychology') was beginning, also interested in questions of intelligence. It stands to reason that, if you want to pursue an agenda that shows whites/males/upper classes are more intelligent than others, you need a way of measuring intelligence. One of the first British psychologists and key architects of the rise of intelligence testing, Charles Spearman (1863–1945) is credited with creating a theory of intelligence that could be measured by tests (psychometric testing). From analysis of multiple tests, he theorised that variations in people's scores seemed to be explainable by just two factors: he believed people had a general ability level in thinking (which he labelled 'g'), as well as a specific ability related to the particular task at hand.

Spearman's theory has an interesting link to the 'tree' image of learning we offered with Dogma A. Recent theories of multiple intelligence (e.g. logical, visual-spatial, verbal, etc.) have clear links back to such images. Theories that children have different learning styles also have a link to the notion that we have specific intelligences and abilities in different spheres. However, learning styles have been largely discredited.

Spearman's theory of intelligence connected directly to the rise of intelligence testing, the idea being that if we have a general intelligence, 'g', then it would be helpful to try to measure that. This is precisely what IQ (intelligence quotient) tests are designed to do, by assessing competence across a range of different skills and then analysing what value of 'g' gives the best explanation of the scores.

Recent neuroscience has invalidated Spearman's model of intelligence. Furthermore, it has also become clear that intelligence testing via IQ tests contains significant biases towards middle-class culture. In other words, items on IQ tests have been found to contain cultural and historical assumptions that make them less accessible to children from low socio-economic backgrounds, compared with children from higher ones. Despite such glaring flaws, the idea of intelligence seems to be strongly embedded in society and folk psychology.

The danger of misusing the idea of 'intelligence' could not have had a starker illustration than the shameful history of intelligence-testing in the early twentieth century. At that time, testing was linked to notions of trying to improve the 'stock' of a nation's genetic pool, as well as a more overtly racist sense of keeping heredity lines 'pure'. In the United States, committees for the 'Sterilization of the Feeble Minded' operated in the twentieth century, resulting in tens of thousands of citizens being coercively sterilised, predominantly white working-class women. Incredibly, sterilisation based on 'intelligence' in the USA actually gathered pace in the 1970s, with the practice finally ending in 1981.

While practices of sterilisation and the idea of 'breeding out' human traits now appear abhorrent, the notion of 'intelligence' used to justify those practices appears to be as strongly held as ever, as a perspective on human capabilities. In other words, while sterilisation was an appalling programme affecting those seen as being at the bottom of a fictitious and inherently biased IQ ladder, the erroneous idea that there *is* an IQ ladder is still commonly held to this day. One specific example of the continued impact of Spearman's views of intelligence is the grouping of students according to their perceived 'ability' in a subject. To cast this practice in its historical terms, setting is a way of keeping the supposedly 'strong-minded' together and free from interference by the supposedly 'feeble-minded'.

Setting practices

One direct consequence of the myth of intelligence and the related dogma that 'Maths is for some people, not others' is the prevalence of 'setting', commonly used in English schools. In maths lessons, we have routinely grouped the 'highers' together on a table, and then similar 'ability' children on tables all the way down to the 'lowers', who despite attempts to mask their group name, always know who they are. And in larger primary schools, particularly in the later years, students have frequently been placed in different classrooms based on 'ability'.

We know that once children are placed on the 'bottom table' or in the 'bottom set', there is rarely any movement out of that position. We know that such placements have a high degree of error, even when judged with an independent attainment test. We know that children of colour and children from low socio-economic backgrounds are disproportionately represented within lower sets. We know that 'lower' groups tend to be given more routine and repetitive work than their peers, with less opportunity for creative thinking or problem-solving. The situation is summed up well by *The Simpsons*, with Bart being sent to a 'remedial' class and complaining: 'Let me get this straight, we're behind the rest of our class and we're going to catch up to them by going slower than they are?' (www.youtube.com/watch?v=5wguuKpRJRE).

But the consequences of setting are far from amusing. We know that failure in school maths can have devastating life consequences, both in terms of self-esteem and in terms of access to higher education and further qualification, and that such barriers can lead to cycles of generational disadvantage. In England every year, around 20 per cent of children aged 16 do not reach a level of mathematical proficiency judged internationally as necessary for participation as an active citizen in a technological society. This is a shockingly high proportion and, so far, no attempts to change it have succeeded.

In England, one consequence of the 'mastery' approach to mathematics introduced soon after the 2014 curriculum change has been a push towards 'mixed' or 'mixed-attainment' or 'mixed ability' classrooms in primary and secondary school. It's welcome that setting practices are being questioned, in a way they have not been for many decades. Our concern is, unless we come to think about 'ability' or 'intelligence' differently, there is a danger that no matter what classroom arrangement we use, there will still be an implicit categorising of children according to preconceptions of what they can and cannot do. And if there's one thing we know about human relations in a school context, it is that we tend to meet the expectations put upon us.

From intelligence to mindset?

A theory that has caught the attention of many school staffrooms in England (as well as in the USA and in Canada) since it was developed – and one that's potentially an antidote to the concept of intelligence – is the idea that humans have either a 'fixed' or a 'growth' mindset. This distinction was coined by the American psychologist Carol Dweck and has been championed by the mathematics educator Jo Boaler. A fixed mindset is linked to the belief we are born with a general ability we can't change (e.g. as per Spearman's theory of intelligence). A fixed mindset involves seeing mistakes as a confirmation of the view that we don't have the ability to succeed. A growth mindset comes from a belief that we can develop new skills and competences through our own learning. From a growth mindset, failure may be painful, but it's used in a positive manner to help define new priorities for learning. As an initial question mark about these definitions, we note that behaviour which might indicate a fixed mindset could equally come from having experienced repeated failure or disadvantage, and coming to the conclusion that, given the circumstances, it's not worth trying any more. Mistakes might be experienced, not as a confirmation of lacking the required 'ability', but as indicating a lack of insight into the implicit 'rules of the game' of schooling (which, of course, tends to be middle-class rules of politeness, etc.).

There have been a number of school initiatives and interventions designed to promote a productive use of mistakes by children, in the hope of cultivating a growth mindset. Instead of testing IQ, there are now tests of a child's 'mindset' and the extent to which it is growth or fixed. A meta-study in 2018 (i.e. a study that collated other studies) found:

- only weak links between measures of a child's growth mindset and their achievement in school
- little effect from mindset interventions on children's academic achievement.

But there was evidence that, for students from low socio-economic backgrounds, there may be some benefit from mindset interventions. Several subsequent studies have also shown little impact of mindset interventions, but slightly better results for more disadvantaged students.

Overall, despite the attractiveness of the distinction between mindsets, it appears their use in schools isn't having the kind of transformational effect which was hoped for. It could be that the interventions themselves need to improve. There is a slight logical conundrum, as you might need a growth mindset to get out of being in a fixed mindset, so it's not quite clear how someone might shift away from fixed thinking. The idea of mindset and its measurement feels close to the ideas of intelligence covered earlier, in that a mindset seems to be something we 'have', so it operates with a similar logic to IQ measures. Perhaps part of the attractiveness and uptake of the mindsets idea is precisely because it fits historical ideas of intelligence, which are embedded in our society and ways of thinking.

Through our work, we've become wary of anything that might reinforce binary thinking about children, i.e. classifying children into one of two groups. The description of 'higher' children, from the start of this chapter, could serve as a definition of 'growth mindset' children. And similarly, the description of 'lower' children, could serve to define having a 'fixed mindset'. While as a teacher, thinking 'mindset' has a more hopeful sense of possibilities for change than 'highers/lowers', it might still lead to classifying children into those who are acting as desired and those who show some 'deficits'. Deficit models – thinking about what people lack – tend to marginalise the already marginalised. Moving beyond the dogma that 'some people are maths people' means moving away from binary thinking about children. We imagine no one would want to be categorised into a binary of 'good versus bad' as a teacher, parent or partner. We know in our own lives that circumstances lead us to act differently with varying skill and wisdom at different times, and in different contexts, so any global judgment would be unfair and misleading.

And yet global judgments are precisely what we make about children's mathematics, reinforced by the dogma that 'some people are maths people'. In fact, when we say that some people are maths people, we're assigning them a specific characteristic, in the same way we might say that they're tall or blond or British. We are saying something about their identity, and when we do that, we tend to assume that such attributes are fairly objective, fixed traits. In the image on the left below, we see a person, 'me', and to that person we can attach a bunch of labels that describe them. In reality, nobody is fixed and static (or so perfectly round!). We move, we breathe, we age and so on. Furthermore, we are always doing these things within an environment, and it's difficult to separate ourselves from that environment: we'd be very different living on the moon, where gravity is weaker; we'd be very different if we'd grown up with older siblings or none. What if we imagine ourselves as processes or events, rather than still objects? What if we imagine ourselves as porous and extended, to show how we shape and are shaped by our environment? The image on the right attempts to express that idea of 'me' in terms of what I do, where I go, how I behave, instead of in terms of who I am. The curves in the line are responses to certain constraints in the environment, pushing me in one direction or the other, while I also leave traces, thereby marking the environment.

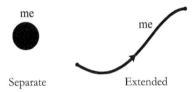

Separate   Extended

Rethinking intelligence

So, what *does* it mean if we catch ourselves thinking that someone is intelligent? How can we think about differences in ways that aren't negative? Thinking about the example of maths, learning from any situation seems to require the capacity to 'stay with it' long enough for ideas to formulate. To learn something new, we need to be able to tolerate ambiguity and a state of not-knowing first. But we all have plenty of mechanisms, in all walks of life, for not putting ourselves in this position. For example, as adults we often develop habitual defensive phrases such as, 'Oh, I'm not an organised person', as a way of avoiding the issue of how we might change the situation. We are all fixed in some aspects of our lives.

In order to learn successfully, there must be a willingness to tolerate ambiguities and the spaces and times of not knowing. Different children will feel comfortable with this at different moments of their lives. Over time, these feelings might solidify into attitudes or habits. And then it might seem as though one child is simply more naturally gifted than another, has more 'ability' or more 'intelligence'. What we want to emphasise here is that these impressions will have been a long time coming, and that they are not to do with a child's potential and are never fixed.

Thinking about children in terms of talents or intelligence means thinking that they 'have' certain things others don't. When we see learning as an act of possession, it's perhaps inevitable that we classify children into those who have and those who have not 'got' the concept, the ability, the intelligence, the mindset. If we think about a child's understanding of a concept on the curriculum, there will always be *some* understanding – it's surely never static and we can be certain that no two people have exactly the same understanding. Instead of thinking about learning as a possession, an alternative metaphor is one of learning as participating (not static like the point, but active like the line). Thinking about learning as participating directs the focus away from what we might or might not 'have' and towards how we can act in a situation. The possession or 'having' metaphor of learning invokes an image of an isolated child, alone with their abilities and facing the world. The participation metaphor of learning immediately brings the context into play and invokes questions, such as what tools are available, and how others might be participating as well. If we view learning as participating, we know that sometimes, participating in a task (such as a sport) clicks and flows and at other times, it doesn't. And so, in learning, we might be more tolerant of someone having an 'off' day and not seeming to get something, without making a judgment about their intelligence.

Listening choices

A focus on what children can and cannot do as individuals takes place against a backdrop of adult or curriculum expectations. If we want to find out what pupils know, with this idea of possession, we're probably looking at how what children say fits our frameworks or assumptions about what understanding looks like in a particular context. One way to think differently about learning is to work on listening differently, as we mentioned in Dogma B. It might seem odd to consider choices about how we listen, but in a maths classroom, there are some significantly different possibilities.

Almost anyone who has spent time in a primary classroom will have experienced interactions in which a teacher asks a question (e.g. 'What is seven times eight?'), a child answers ('Fifty-six!') and the teacher judges their answer ('Great, well done!'). Such a sequence might confirm for the teacher that the child has (possesses) age-appropriate times–table knowledge. Asking a question when you already know the answer is an unusual conversational form, generally only found in teaching and learning contexts. Brent Davis studied forms of teacher listening for his PhD thesis and would label the listening of the teacher in this example as *evaluative*. The teacher has an answer in mind and gives the child feedback according to whether the child's response matches the teacher's intention. There isn't much the child could say in this situation that might make the teacher change their mind about what constitutes a correct or incorrect performance.

Even subtle shifts from the starting question, 'What is seven times eight?' can allow for other forms of listening and conversation. For instance, the question 'How would you work out seven times eight?' is more open – the teacher doesn't know what responses will follow and doesn't have one idea in mind. A conversation in the classroom might go like this:

Teacher:	How would you work out seven times eight? I don't want the answer; I want to know how you would get the answer.
First child:	I just know it.
Teacher:	You just know it. It can be helpful to have some facts that you can simply recall, thank you. Anyone have a different means?
Second child:	I count up in sevens.
Teacher:	Would you write anything down or do it in your head?
Second child:	In my head.
Teacher:	Okay, we might try that in a moment all together. Anyone have a different method?
Third child:	I would work out five eights and count up from there.

The teacher's listening here is non-evaluative – there's no judgement about the correctness or otherwise of the responses. A focus on methods rather than answers is one mechanism for supporting non-evaluative listening. Instead of evaluating single answers from individual pupils, a range of methods can be collected and their strengths and weaknesses compared. The shift from 'What is …?' to 'How would you work out …?' can make the question a genuine one for the teacher. You can shift from teaching one 'best' method towards children having a range of approaches, to be used flexibly. Children's responses can act as resources and ideas for one another, instead of only being a way for the teacher to assess 'ability'. You could collect children's responses on a board, in order to provide a set of tools for other pupils to try.

It might seem scary to ask a question and not know what kind of response or reply you'll get. There can be safety in evaluative listening, particularly if you yourself have some anxiety about maths. You know where you are, and you know how you'll respond to any possible answer, because the only options are right or wrong. A shift to focusing on methods immediately requires the teacher to handle unforeseen responses, where it might not be immediately obvious if the method will work.

In research we have done with primary teachers, one safety mechanism to help support non-evaluative ways of listening has been to invoke the idea of 'thinking mathematically' or 'thinking like a mathematician'. We've worked in classrooms where teachers have told their classes that the overall purpose of the year's study is to learn to 'think mathematically'. Over time in these classrooms, the term 'thinking mathematically', or 'thinking like a mathematician', gets linked to a range of attributes such as asking questions, noticing patterns, making predictions and not being afraid to make mistakes. The 'learning as participating' metaphor is relevant again here. A classroom can become a site for participating in mathematical activity, defined by processes as well as content.

Focusing on a set of skills to develop, which sit alongside the content, can be used to support 'getting alongside' the children in a classroom. We've observed teachers hearing a child's idea, being unsure if the idea will work, and saying something like: 'Well, if we are thinking mathematically about this, what can we do to see if it will work?' With a few prompts, the child might be able to work through their method or idea, perhaps with a partner or as something for the whole class to consider. We've observed that a focus on developing mathematical skills frees teachers from the self-imposed pressure to have an immediate answer for, and evaluation of, anything said by a child in a maths lesson. Everyone in the class can be invited to try on the mantle of a mathematician: the mantle of a 'maths person'.

Non-evaluative listening is a skill which pretty much any primary teacher will recognise and already uses frequently. But we suspect that, in some contexts, non-evaluative listening is reserved for lessons covering art, drama, literature and music. One way to loosen the hold of thinking in terms of ability is to find ways to bring these non-evaluative listening skills to teaching maths. Perhaps when we think of some pupils as 'maths people', we're simply only pointing to those children who get on well in an environment of evaluative listening.

Non-evaluative listening might seem a lot more time-consuming than just giving an evaluation or telling people what to do, and we're conscious of the pressures even at primary school to cover the required content in each year of study. We're proposing the need for at least some moments in lessons where there can be a dwelling on issues, a collective pause, a chance for making sense together. The primary teacher Caroline Ormesher has written about the need for a 'slow pedagogy' in teaching and learning mathematics (Ormesher, 2021). We'll address in the next chapter how it might be possible to dwell on and be slow in maths lessons, while also covering the necessary curriculum content.

A communal mathematics

One further way to reimagine education away from the focus on children's abilities is to consider what a more 'communal' mathematics might look like. If a pupil can't complete a set task, rather than (or as well as) using that information to log their current state of progress or development, we can also ask what tool or resource this child needs to be successful. There is a strange ban on the use of some tools in maths classrooms. We wouldn't usually stop a child using pen and paper to solve a complex problem or using our place-value number system as a tool (except in cases of learning about, for instance, Roman numerals). Yet we frequently deny other tools, such as number charts, access to talking with other children or calculators, to name a few. Lulu Healy, British professor of mathematics education, has pointed out that these divisions of acceptable and unacceptable tools are both arbitrary and, usually without intention, likely to disadvantage some groups of learners, such as blind or deaf learners, those who have difficulty in processing long lists of instructions or those who have difficulty in memorising arbitrary facts.

One communal activity is the use of 'chanting' in the classroom, based around the tool of a number chart. Chanting is often seen as linked to rote learning and memorisation. Our image of chanting is a bit different. One tool we have both used for classroom chanting is a tens chart designed by Caleb Gattegno.

1	2	3	4	5	6	7	8	9
10	20	30	40	50	60	70	80	90
100	200	300	400	500	600	700	800	900
1,000	2,000	3,000	4,000	5,000	6,000	7,000	8,000	9,000
10,000	20,000	30,000	40,000	50,000	60,000	70,000	80,000	90,000
100,000	200,000	300,000	400,000	500,000	600,000	700,000	800,000	900,000

If your class is unfamiliar with the chart, it can be used to work on number naming. You could tap on a number and ask the class to say its name back in unison. With younger children, we'd initially avoid the tens row, as this is the only irregularly named row in the whole system in English. England's Mastery Professional Development Materials also suggest working on naming numbers from 20 to 100 before returning to the 11–19 range.

In time, the teacher might tap on '300', '60' and then '8', and the children say 'three hundred (and) sixty-eight' back. This might continue for a while, exploring different combinations. We've found it can be effective to get into a routine with a class of doing five to ten minutes a day of some communal, spoken work with the chart.

You could tap on a number and get children to chant back the number that's one greater or one less; perhaps then ten greater or ten less; one hundred greater and so on. This could extend to writing – for example, children choose a starting number and, with a focus on three less, they write out what happens to their number if you keep on taking away three.

You can bring pupils' attention to the movements needed to tap out numbers and operations on those numbers (such as adding one). Some primary teachers print off small charts for their pupils to gesture along with the chorus. Or a child could lead a chant by doing the pointing at the front, on a large chart. The chart makes clear how our written number system is structured and how the number names mostly follow a regular, ordered pattern. Choral work offers the possibility for pupils to be carried along by each other. It's possible for a child to drop out for a while, observe and listen, and then rejoin. Language patterns become apparent through familiarity. If you use the chart regularly and consistently, connections are available to be made at the point children are ready to make them.

In the next chapter, we cover some case studies of practices that draw away from the idea of ability, intelligence or mindsets as relatively stable capacities in children (and the assumption that there are maths people and non-maths people), and that represent metaphors of learning that don't involve possession.

Putting into practice D: Towards a communal mathematics

This chapter offers two case studies of classroom practices where there is a communal approach and learning can be seen as a participation or performance, rather than as a possession.

Thinking or talking about children in terms of their 'ability' unintentionally sustains the dogma that only some people are maths people. Looking to what a communal mathematics might involve has led us to ask: what would teaching look like if there was a focus on collective student participation with concepts, rather than on developing individual student understanding of them? We want to propose that an alternative to a focus on understanding does not have to mean a return to rote learning and the mindless repetition of drills, as we hope the case studies will make clear.

Case study of negative numbers

The first case study comes from the teaching and research of Bob Davis, who worked at Rutgers University in the USA. This university is home to a unique video library of maths teaching (http://videomosaic.org) spanning over 50 years, starting with a project instigated by Davis (the 'Madison Project') in the 1960s. Part of this collection is some historic video footage of Davis working with different groups of students. We have chosen to set out one clip here which has been adopted as the suggested way to introduce children to negative numbers in the England's NCETM's Mastery Professional Development Materials. We feel this approach has huge potential. In his TEDX talk of 2021, Alf draws on this video footage in order to question the building-block assumption of Dogma A (www.youtube.com/watch?v=-Gajs_UNItU&t=52s).

In this clip, Bob Davis is teaching children who look around five years old. In the transcript below, RB is Bob Davis, (.) indicates a short pause and (…) a pause of 1 second or more.[1] We recommend you read the transcript slowly as something quite remarkable takes place towards the end, something which the orthodoxy of past learning theories would suggest is impossible: pupils aged five appearing to work fluently with the concept of a negative number. We intersperse the transcript with brief reflections. The clip begins with RB at the front of the class with two children, Nora and Jeff. Nora is holding a bag of stones.

Speaker	Words	Actions
RB:	Okay, Jeff is going to tell us when to start and, you say 'go'.	
Jeff:	Go!	
RB:	Okay, you say go (.) and I'm going to put three stones in the bag that Nora is holding… (.) Three stones in.	RB drops 3 stones in the bag, one by one; we hear them drop.
RB:	Are there more stones in the bag now or less than there were when Jeff said go? (…) Charlotte, what do you say?	
Charlotte:	More.	
RB:	And how many more, as if you all didn't all know, how many more? Laurie?	
Laurie:	Three.	
RB:	Three, huh.	RB writes '3' on the blackboard.

[1]A version of this transcript appeared in Coles (2015).

We puzzled for a long time over the function of getting Jeff to say 'go'. It seemed superfluous and yet Davis was such a careful thinker and teacher that we were sure it was intentional and meaningful. We eventually realised that having a moment in time that is easy to refer to – 'when Jeff said go' – allows a focus on the change in the number of stones from that moment, without needing to know the number of stones in the bag.

Speaker	Words	Actions
RB:	And now I'm going to take some stones out of the bag. How many stones do you want me to take out of the bag? (.) Barbara, how many stones do you want to take out?	Several children raise their hands.
Barbara:	Three.	
RB:	Three, I'll take three out, okay. Barbara says take three out so I'll take three stones out. (.) There's one, (.) there's two, (.) there's three. Three stones out. And I'd better write that.	RB adds to the board, so it now reads '3 − 3 ='
RB:	I took three stones out. Now are there more stones in the bag than there were when Jeff said go or are there less? Er, Brett?	
Brett:	There's the same amount.	
RB:	There's the same amount (.) and I bet that's right and what will I say here as if you didn't all know? (.) Sandy?	RB is pointing with his chalk to the space to the right of the equals sign in '3 − 3 ='
Sandy:	Zero, is what I'll say.	
Others:	Negative zero.	RB writes: '3 − 3 = 0'

Speaker	Words	Actions
RB:	Zero. (.) Okay that was that time. I need two other assistants... (.) Thank you very much.	Nora and Jeff return to their seats.
RB:	I need somebody to hold the bag. (.) Paul, would you come? (.) And I need somebody to say when to go. (.) Bruce, would you come?	Paul and Bruce come to the front.
RB:	You're going to tell us when to start, good.	
Bruce:	Go.	

There is nothing too surprising up to this point. One thing we notice is the beautiful patterning of speech used and the ritual that's developing about how this task runs.

In terms of understanding what happens next, it's crucial to consider what the numbers Davis writes represent. A common response when we show this clip to teachers is that the 3 is the number of stones put in the bag. And while this response seems correct, it also misses some of the subtlety of what is taking place. The 3, when it is written, is the children's response to the question, which becomes something of a mantra in this task: 'Are there more stones in the bag now than when [student name] said go or are there less?' In other words, the 3 represents the *change* in the number of stones in the bag. So, while the children can see stones going in and coming out, what is being symbolised is an action with those objects, not the objects themselves. This seemingly small shift makes all the difference in what happens next.

Speaker	Words	Actions
RB:	Go, Bruce said go. Um, how many stones do you want me to put in the bag? Nancy, how many?	Several children put up their hands.

Speaker	Words	Actions
Nancy:	Five.	
RB:	Five. (.) I'll see if I've got five. Turns out I've got five, I've got five. There's five stones there and I'm going to put all five of these in the bag.	RB lays 5 stones on his palm. He puts them one by one into the bag; we hear each one as it drops.
RB:	And I better write that before I forget.	RB writes '5' on the blackboard.
RB:	Are there more stones in the bag than when, er, Bruce said go or are there less? Jeff?	
Jeff:	More.	
RB:	And how many more?	
Jeff:	Five.	
RB:	Five. (.) Five more huh. Okay, how many do you want me to take out? Nora, how many do you want me to take out?	
Nora:	Five.	
RB:	Er. (.) I don't want to do that. (.) Some other number?	
Nora:	Six.	
RB:	Six, take six out.	
Student:	Did you have stones in the bag to start with?	

Speaker	Words	Actions
RB:	I better have had, hadn't I? (.) I wouldn't be able to do this if I didn't.	RB removes some stones and counts them on his palm.

We don't know if Davis had planned to create the scenario where a child asked for more stones to be taken out than were put in. As one of the other classmates comments, for this to work, you need to have some stones in the bag to start with! The focus on change – the action of putting in and taking out – meant that we didn't need to know how many stones were in the bag until this moment. It is from this point that something remarkable takes place.

Speaker	Words	Actions
RB:	Let's see. (.) One, two, three, four, five, six. (.) That was more good luck than good management. (.) I got exactly six. (.) Okay I'll write it.	RB writes on board: '5 − 6 ='.
RB:	Have I got more stones in the bag than when Bruce said go or have I got less? Jeff, what do you think?	
Jeff:	Less.	
RB:	And anyone know how many less? Nora, how many less?	
Nora:	One less.	
RB:	Okay and how do I write this one to show that it's one less? Ceri.	RB writes: '5 − 6 = 1'.
Ceri:	Negative one.	
RB:	Negative one (.) and that's just what I'll do.	RB writes: '5 − 6 = −1'.

We've shown this clip to many teachers and it's rare that it doesn't provoke astonishment. It's a common idea that the concept of negative numbers is intangible, that it causes confusion and that it's one of the more complex challenges of the primary curriculum for children. Theories of learning inspired by Jean Piaget (see Dogma A), would suggest that children can't work with such concepts until around the age of 11, and yet here we see five- and six-year-olds seemingly doing so with ease.

It's worth trying to unpack what's happening. The first thing to note is that the class is working as a whole group and everyone is engaged in the same task, which takes place at the front of the classroom. Another thing is that there's no discussion or explanation of why the results written on the board are a correct representation of the problem. The symbols accompany the actions with little fuss made about them. The situation for the class is a bit like a game and the video recording shows obvious signs of the pupils enjoying what is taking place.

Focusing on change, not the objects themselves, is a meaningful distinction to make. The key point is that by using numbers to represent a relationship between quantities, not the quantities themselves, Davis opens the way for negative numbers to become as visible and tangible as their positive counterparts. The children can see the 6 stones being taken out, compared with the 5 that were put in, and it is then obvious that there will be 1 fewer stone in the bag than before. And it's here, again, that we see the vital function of the child saying 'go'. We can only consider the change in more or fewer stones, if we have a clear starting point, which the child saying 'go' provides.

From the start of this game, the symbols are abstracted from the objects, because they are associated with relationships while at the same time, they do also refer to the concrete stones used. If teaching a lesson like this, you could also turn pupils' attention to dealing with the symbols in their own right, evoking, if necessary, the actions they represented. In Dogma E we discuss the idea that 'Maths is hard because it is abstract' – certainly the children working with Bob Davis do not seem to be finding the abstract ideas they are working with particularly difficult.

The outcome of the Davis task is that children develop a symbolic fluency with negative numbers that goes well beyond what is usual in the English curriculum for children of that age. We think that what they understand by these symbols isn't necessarily important at this stage.

What matters is that the game allows all children access to be producing or performing mathematical statements, in a way that matches standard conventions for negative numbers. Some children might begin to notice shortcuts for predicting the resulting change, given the number of stones put in and the number taken out. They might be able to link the rules for the symbols to other processes of addition and subtraction they have come across.

Linking symbols to relations, not objects, is an effective general strategy for teaching communal maths. It can be enacted with whole groups. One way of making the links between symbols and relations is to symbolise actions – and perform those actions. This strategy can help to demystify maths, particularly for those who find it harder to access. It makes every pupil into a 'maths person', rather than following the dogma that only some people are maths people. In the example above, rather than negative numbers appearing as mysterious objects that only some people (mathematicians) know about, they are laid bare for everyone to access.

Case study of choral chanting

This second case study comes from the work of Megan Franke, Elham Kazemi and Angela Chan Turrou. In a book we recommend (Franke, Kazemi & Chan Turrou, 2018), Megan Franke and her colleagues set out two core sets of practices for primary mathematics: 'counting collections' and 'choral counting'. The aims of these practices are to support children participating in lessons, by making participation communal. Franke and her colleagues have found that these practices help teachers to listen to children and learn about children's mathematical thinking. They see working on the two forms of counting as a way of enacting their commitment to equity in the classroom and allowing access to the subject for all children, not just those who are seen as the 'maths people'.

We'll focus here on what they mean by 'choral counting', which has strong links to what we called 'chanting' in Dogma D. With choral counting, a teacher chooses a starting number and a number to count up or down by – for example, asking children to start at zero and count up by 15. One key way to make this task successful is to record on a board what the children say – it's important to plan in advance how it will be written. Here's one example of how a board might be ordered for counting by 6. We say *one* example because one strategy you could use is to work with the same choral count sequence but order it differently, such as by varying whether you write it in rows or in columns, or varying how many numbers there are in a row/column.

6 12 18 24 30
36 42 48 54 60
66 72 78 84 90
96 102 108 ...

Children will come in and out of following the count. There can be pauses and you could invite pupils to share their strategies. There are predictable moments of difficulty (e.g. moving over the 100s) and also moments when the count becomes relatively easy again (e.g. 102 to 108). You could take the group back to chant again from an earlier number to get everyone engaged and develop a rhythm that takes them over a hurdle. If the class is finding it more difficult, you could ask pairs to discuss and agree on the next number.

At some point, when you judge that the class have done enough, you can stop the count and invite the pupils to look at the record of their counting on the board, for example, asking, 'What do you notice?' Looking at the numbers above, you might want to ask yourself this question and imagine in advance what children in a primary classroom might say. Some of the patterns may help children to predict a number that is not yet written. For instance, someone might notice a pattern in the numbers in the right-hand column, that they look like the 3 times table, and predict that the next one will be 120. You can also ask why the patterns work. In the case of the right-hand column, why might these numbers be going up in 30s? And this is where different ways of recording the count will lend themselves to different patterns being noticed.

The possibilities for this kind of choral counting are limitless. As suggested above, counts can start at any number, and increase or decrease in any number. It is surprising what can be noticed from counting in 1s. An example (from Franke et al.) used with first-grade children is counting in 1s from 92 to 135, where the numbers were recorded horizontally, moving to the row below, so that the ones digits lined up. Later on, children can go up in 10s or 100s, or in 0.1s, or in 0.5s. They can start at zero and go down in 2s, or start at 1089 and go down in 7s.

Choral counting can be joyful and playful, and taps into children's interest in big numbers and patterns. It can be a way of giving children access to some of the regularities of the number system, which can be lost in the focus on the irregularly named numbers 11–19. The communal aspect of the activity can act as a small counterweight to the pulls towards individualism in many Western societies. Chanting, or chorusing, together speaks to communal ways of being, and a communal sense of responsibility, something familiar to many indigenous ways of knowing. It is not individuals who are, or are not maths people; rather we struggle together and we are maths people together.

Summary

The history of the dogma that 'Maths is for some people, not others' was linked to discredited views of human intelligence. Recent ideas about mindsets, and encouraging children to have a growth mindset, are positive in that they shift away from seeing intelligence as a fixed capacity. However, the idea of a mindset continues the assumption that intelligence or ability in a subject is something internal to each individual pupil. These views don't consider the environment pupils live in. Anyone's ability to do something is directly linked to their past experiences, the interactions they've had around the subject, the resources they have available and more. But it's all too easy to slip into thinking that children have particular abilities (or mindsets) in a subject and, without meaning to, assume that these characteristics won't easily change. We know that adverse childhood experiences can damage a child's opportunities for learning and that successful interventions can make a radical difference to their ability to learn. And yet it can be hard to hold our minds open to the potential and possibilities of each of our pupils.

This chapter included two case studies of communal maths tasks which have a less individualistic focus than usual. In both cases, there are tasks for children to engage in communally. Mathematical symbols are introduced to represent relationships that are visible, or actions that are performed. Pupils perform maths, with an emphasis on using symbols correctly, rather than on what and whether they have understood. Dick Tahta, a maths educator and the inspirational teacher of Stephen Hawking, once advised teachers to 'take care of the symbols and the sense will take care of itself'. In other words, if we take care to set up situations in which children are engaging in sophisticated use of symbols, and those symbols are linked to meaningful actions, then children will do all the sense-making we want.

Dogma E:
'Maths is hard because it is abstract'

Alf's story

I sometimes talk with my niece about what she's doing in maths lessons at her primary school. One day, when she was about five, her parents messaged me in exasperation, having got into a huge argument with her about maths. The conversation had gone like this:

Daughter: If you count down, below zero, what number do you get?

Father: You get minus one.

Daughter: No, I don't want to know what I have to do, I want to know the name.

Father: It's minus one.

Daughter: NO! What is it?! What's its name?

In this conversation, my niece shows that she appreciates the difference between the object '−1' and the process of subtracting one. One source of confusion in maths is that the same symbol is almost always used for both an object (e.g. '−1' as a position on a number line) and the process (e.g. '−1' as movement on a number line). Sometimes we try to differentiate between process and object in language, e.g. using 'negative one' for the object, and 'minus one' for the process. (I wonder if 'negative one' might have satisfied my niece as to the name?)

Whatever occurred in this conversation, it seems certain that the difficulties for my niece were not to do with anything being too abstract. In fact, it's almost the opposite: she was being highly abstract – at age five – in making a distinction between the result of an operation and the operation itself. This story surely gives the lie to the idea that young children aren't able to think about abstract ideas and structures.

In the domain of art, the word 'abstract' was used to mark a turn away from representational art, which is art that depicts people and landscapes and events. A good example is the 80 cm by 80 cm *Black Square* on a white background by Russian artist Kazimir Malevich. Rather than working through recognition or imitation, inspiring viewers by the likeness of the art to the real-world counterpart, abstract artists sought to express different realities of life, often foregrounding primary concepts like colour or form. The black square expresses a sense of pure, disembodied thought, which can be felt as a well of sheer possibility.

The meanings of the word 'abstract' can help us both to understand what it might mean for maths to be abstract and to challenge the assumption that abstract means difficult. Etymologically, to abstract means 'to draw away from', 'to cut off'. Maths is seen by many as being cut off or distanced from our everyday experiences of the world, much in the same way that abstract art is distanced from the people, places and events commonly represented in representational art. Interestingly, and perhaps even famously, abstract art is often considered quite easy to make, which implies that being abstract is not necessarily connected to being difficult. However, what is often difficult, at least for the viewer, is understanding what the artwork is about, or being confident that you've experienced it in the 'right' way. There aren't usually many cues about how to interpret it, and very little feedback available either within or outside of an art gallery.

All of these things are also true in some way or another about maths, which doesn't always seem to relate to the people, places and events of everyday life. It is not always clear to 'viewers' what maths is really about. And, in some ways, maths is quite easy. Like the black square, it doesn't have to take into account the nuances and complexities of life: when you solve a problem about dividing a cake, you don't have to worry about the crumbs, the icing, whether the knife is good enough to cut evenly, and so on – not to mention how the division is affected by the temperature, the guests with dietary requirements or the size of the plates. Abstract division in maths is in many ways *much easier* than real-life contexts of division. However, there are also fewer cues in maths. First, you have to recognise that it's division that needs to be done. And then, there is less feedback than in real life on whether the cake-dividing was successful.

By evoking abstract art, we're trying to say that in some ways, maths is hard because it is abstract *and*, in other ways, maths is easy because it is abstract. We'll return to this theme later in the chapter when we discuss teaching approaches that focus on the use of 'real-world' problems in the classroom as a way of reducing the abstract nature of maths. But for now, we'll explore how the word 'abstract' has come to be associated with being 'hard' when used to describe maths. Following this, we consider different ways of thinking about the abstract that could help challenge this dogma.

How abstract became associated with a stage in cognitive development

The idea that the abstract is something that can be distinguished from the concrete, and also that abstract thinking is something we develop over time after concrete thinking, appeared in the mid-twentieth century, largely thanks to the work of the Swiss psychologist Jean Piaget. In his experimental work, during which he asked children to solve various kinds of problems, he formulated hypotheses about how their mathematical thinking developed. These hypotheses became known as Piaget's stage theory – the idea that development from infancy to adolescence occurs in four stages, beginning with the sensorimotor stage and ending with the formal operational stage.

Whether or not Piaget was correct, the word 'abstract' emerged at a crucial time in European thinking about education – post-war, with the regularisation of mandatory schooling for everyone. Abstract thinking came to be seen as something only older children could accomplish and was associated with theoretical or hypothetical thinking, rather than empirical. Because it was associated with the last stage of development, the idea that thinking moved from concrete to abstract became well entrenched.

Since Piaget's tasks were so central to his theorising, it is worth taking a look at them in order to better understand how the notion of abstract became associated with a stage of development. In a balance task, Piaget asked children of different ages to balance a scale by hooking different weights onto each end of the scale, as shown below. As you can see, the location of each hook in relation to the other is what makes this task challenging. It was only the 13-year-old children (and older) who were successful in solving the task. Whereas the five-year-olds did not succeed in solving the task, the seven-years-olds could place the weights on each side, but did not take into account the locations of the hooks on the scale. The 10-years-olds could only solve the task through trial and error. The 13-year-olds, however, could come up with a relation between the location of the weights and their size, which they could use to solve the task. In other words, what was deemed abstract was when the children could predict the solution without having to experiment. With this 'hands-off' thinking, the 13-year-old students were seen as being able to consider the consequences of actions not yet undertaken.

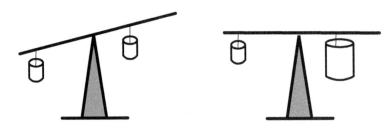

Since Piaget's work, many researchers have challenged stage theory, both in broad terms (arguing that it is not age-dependent, for example), but also in relation to specific findings. (It might depend on how you ask the question, or on the nature of the task – indeed, children much younger than 13-year-olds have been found to engage in the kind of hypothetical thinking that Piaget associated with the formal operational stage.)

The Russian psychologist Lev Vygotsky had a different perspective on the abstract. He believed that all concepts begin as abstract and only become concrete through experience and over time. A child's understanding of a concept such as love or courage starts off as idealised, with little nuance and few links to real events – in other words, with characteristics we often see as 'abstract'. Over time, a child's idea of courage or love becomes more concrete through many differing connections and relations to people and events, and can be recognised even when it has different qualities at different times. Therefore, the abstractness of the concept shows its absence of relations or connections: the more connections, the more concrete something is. And concrete doesn't imply that we're talking about something physical or tactile, since we can also develop very concrete understandings of concepts like 'love' and 'courage'. If Vygotsky's ideas had dominated the anglophone world of maths education in the 1950s, we might well have ended up with a different dogma, perhaps something along the lines of 'Maths is hard because it is disconnected' or even 'Maths is hard because it is concrete'!

But with the dogma we do have, we tend to think of the progression of mathematics learning as being like an arrow, moving from the concrete to the abstract. When we employ 'arrow thinking', we are assuming that there is a one-directional, linear progression In the context of maths learning, we tend to think the same way, namely to assume that learning starts at a certain initial position (not knowing number) and then evolves to a final end-point of understanding the concept of number. In this chapter, we offer a different spatial imaginary that requires shifting our point of view to look at things from a different perspective, as shown in the image on the right.

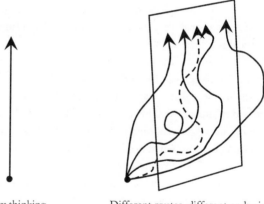

Arrow thinking   Different routes, different endpoints

Indeed, if we look at the arrow from the sideview, we might actually see that the path of learning depends on particular kinds of relations – and that the endpoints might thus be different depending on which path was taken. We might experience zero by experimenting with subtraction; and, we might experience zero by riding down the elevator to the ground floor. Even though we use the same name for all the experiences – the word 'zero' – we cannot ignore the actual relations that each experience has produced – and how zero has become concrete through them. Compared with the arrow then, the image on the right evokes less one-dimensionality, less linearity, and less sense that there is only one path along which learning can take place.

When abstract becomes a relational quality

In 1980, Seymour Papert published a book called *Mindstorms* (1980), which was the beginning of the digital technology revolution in mathematics education. In it, Papert describes Logo, which was a programming language that young children could use to move a turtle on the screen. They could create simple shapes like a square, but also more complex ones. In reflecting on students' mathematical work with this 'turtle geometry', Uri Wilensky was struck by the flexibility and engagement with which children were manipulating symbols and numbers. If these things were so abstract, he wondered, shouldn't students be having more difficulty or be shying away from them?

Wilensky resolved his quandary by proposing that things in and of themselves are not abstract or concrete, but that it is the relation between a child and a thing that can be seen as abstract or concrete (Wilensky, 1991). Like love, courage, monsters and dinosaurs, the commands used to make a square – which looked like this: repeat 4 [fd 10 rt 90] – did not exist physically in a way that could be touched, so they may not have been concrete in and of themselves. However, the children forged relations with those symbols. The 90 degrees might be seen as an abstract mathematical concept (indeed, in many curricula, it is introduced to 11–12-year-olds), but when it was used as a way of turning one's own body – with and through the turtle – the concept of an angle became very concrete. These relations involved both feeling and knowing: children knew that a right turn by 90 degrees could help them make a square; they could feel what that right turn was like, putting themselves in the place of the turtle to make the turn.

For Wilensky, and Papert before him, the power of turtle geometry, was precisely in the way it could operate between the physical and virtual worlds, thereby giving rise to new relations that might be harder to forge in the paper-and-pencil world of school mathematics. Indeed, Papert and, especially Sherry Turkle, celebrated the new empirical ways of learning that using Logo afforded. Instead of just knowing the right formula, or memorising a fact, Logo was an environment for testing out ideas, making mistakes and then fixing them. They saw this as a different way of knowing, one in which both thinking and feeling could matter.

In the binary logic we have inherited, the abstract is linked with thinking and the concrete with feeling. Popular culture has fuelled this stereotype. Think of Spock in *Star Trek*, whose logical prowess went hand in hand with his non-emotional personality. These stereotypes ripple into everyday assumptions about scientists being cold, hard, stern people who do not let their feelings get in the way. They are evident in the drawings that children make when asked to 'draw a scientist' or 'draw a mathematician' (as in the research conducted by John Berry and Susan Picker, 2000). Mathematicians and scientists are portrayed as dishevelled, nerdy, male and sometimes even violent people.

However, recent neuroscientific research seems to support the position argued by Turkle and Papert, that thinking and feeling are inextricably linked. More specifically, the neuroscientist Antonio Damasio has shown, using brain lesion research, that people who cannot feel cannot make decisions. Some mathematicians have even written about their feelings about maths. Keith Devlin describes mathematics as a soap opera, because it deals with the relationships between objects such as numbers and shapes. 'What can X do to Y? If X does this to Y, what will Y do back to X? It's got characters, it's got plot, it's got relationships between them, and it's got life and emotion and passion and love and hate' (Devlin, 2000).

If experiencing maths as a soap opera can make it feel more relatable and concrete, then how can we enable these kinds of experiences? Is it by making mathematics more relevant to learners' everyday lives, like showing how maths can be used in sports or while shopping? Not really. These pedagogical approaches certainly help learners to see how maths can be used outside of the classroom and might spark their interest, if the context is one they know and care about. But it doesn't always prompt learners to care about numbers or triangles or fractions or graphs. Let's consider a different approach, which we'll call soap opera maths.

Soap opera maths

The setting: a primary school classroom
The characters: learners, a teacher, a chalkboard, chalk,
    a small 'curtain' (a piece of paper), an equation, some numbers, +, =
The intrigue: missing addend problems

The teacher has written the following equation on the
chalkboard: $5 + \square = 12$. Before she has even turned her head
to face the class, someone shouts out '17'. She expected this,
because she's heard the same answer many times before. Having no
experience with equations of this kind, learners typically do what
they have done before in similar situations, which is to calculate the
sum of the given numbers.

Smiling to herself, the teacher walks over to her desk and gets her
little curtain. Returning to the chalkboard, she makes sure that no
one can see what she is writing, but also makes sure that she can be
heard writing on the chalkboard with her chalk. She then places the
little curtain on the board and steps back so that the pupils can see
what she has done:

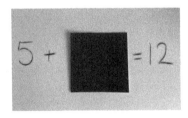

She says, 'I did a calculation, but then I hid one of the numbers
using this curtain. What was the number I hid?'

The curtain suggests some mystery: the missing number is hidden,
but it is part of a story that the pupils know well, which is writing
an addition problem from left to right, calculating the sum at the
end. Somebody, in this case the teacher, has solved the problem
(here, $5 + 7 = $) and the result was 12. Now that the second addend
is covered by a curtain, the learners must solve the riddle: what is
the number under the curtain?

The curtain gives an interesting air of mystery to this problem. But hiding the number isn't just to catch learners' attention. It also helps them to access a story they have experience with, and to use that story to help them solve the problem – to see the relation between the numbers in a new way.

The soap opera maths example involved a micro-story that featured both mathematical characters and elements of plot. But stories can be told at many different levels, across a single lesson, a whole unit or even the entire curriculum. Inspired by the pedagogical potential of seeing maths this way, Leslie Dietiker has developed a story framework for designing lessons, where the characters and students' feelings about what happens to them are taken into consideration *alongside* the target mathematical concepts (Dietiker, 2012). This doesn't mean having to write novels – it's more about how the characters, relations and actions can be emphasised. For example, when moving from counting to addition in the curriculum, characters can be spotlighted by introducing them, perhaps on cards, from 1 to 10. Then a teacher could ask, 'Let's take two of these numbers, like 3 and 4, placing the other cards down. What could they do together?' One child might say that they could be friends 'because they are close to the same age'. This would highlight the fact they're consecutive numbers and that if 3 and 4 are friends, then 4 and 5 must be friends too. This helps pupils focus on ordinal relations between numbers (how one number follows or precedes another, rather than what its size is) and the conversation could continue into larger numbers. A new relation could be suggested, since it is sometimes nice to have many friends. So maybe 3 not only has 2 and 4 as friends, but also 1 and 5. But another pupil might say that 3 and 4 could join forces and become 7, another number on the cards. This might lead to questions such as: 'Are there other numbers that can join forces to make 7?', 'Can 7 join forces with anyone?', 'What numbers can join forces to make 1?' or 'What about 0?' Maybe new actions are needed! As numbers join forces, new cards could be made. Maybe they need to be laid out along a line. There will probably be some holes, at which point some learners might be charged with figuring out how to fill them.

By thinking of mathematical objects as characters and the operations as actions that can reveal new relationships, engaging with number – even simply with the symbols – becomes a concrete experience. The feelings generated in these experiences come both through the connections, since they involve pupils, and also through emotional events that generate surprise or intrigue.

Storytelling is a powerful way of making relations. As Jerome Bruner has shown, humans have a tendency to impose stories on things that happen; we like to find a starting point, identify a cause and, in doing so, we tie different events together into a narrative. This often makes things easier to remember, while also often incorporating some drama or morality. Perhaps this doesn't often happen in the maths classroom because not much is perceived to be happening! When numbers and shapes are presented as static objects, it's not surprising that pupils' urge to make up stories is reduced, or that the only stories they tell are about their own lack of success or understanding.

Stories help us create connections so, without stories, it's not surprising that maths seems abstract to many people. Some pupils manage to create stories of their own in order to remember or make sense of mathematical ideas, but that can be challenging when maths is seen as a set of disconnected things that just need memorising. In other words, rather than assuming that maths is hard because it's abstract, we might say that maths is hard *when there are no connections*. And making connections often takes time, just like making friends does: time to notice, to wonder, to marvel at a huge number, at an unusual shape, at a new symbol – time to allow space for what the mathematician Alfred North Whitehead called 'the romantic phase of mathematical experience', before rushing to precision or generalisation.

Moving mathematics

Another secret to prompting storying can be found by inspecting another dimension of the dogma that 'Maths is hard because it is abstract', which is the association between the abstract and the mental. Through various historical forces, the highest form of reason and intelligence has slowly become associated with the rational, objective and unsentimental mind. From this point of view, the idea of children sitting still at their desks in a classroom is consistent with what's often thought of as the best methods or requirements for thinking mathematically: reflection, contemplation, quietness, stillness. This impression is fed by portrayals of mathematicians sitting alone at their desks in popular culture such as films, with the only hint of movement being hurried and mysterious scribbles on the page. From this, it's easy to conclude that maths is something you do all on your own, with no other people and no other things. The mathematician is seen as being cut off – abstracted – from the world.

This image isn't entirely false; there's certainly a lot of solitary work in maths. But it ignores the crowds of people and objects and actions that always accompany each and every mathematician. Just because these crowds aren't always visible does not mean that they are absent. The people might include mathematicians of the past, and their way of thinking about specific concepts, or colleagues who said something at a conference or made a diagram in the lunchroom or mentioned a connected problem. The objects can be physical, like compasses or computer screens, or they could be symbols and graphs – these are objects that 'talk back' to mathematicians, inviting them to move in a different direction or ask a different question. The actions can be virtual too, such as transformations, or they can be physical, like drawing, gesturing or re-enacting the movement of mathematical objects.

Researchers are studying how our everyday physical experiences in the world contribute to our understanding of mathematical concepts. The experience of walking along a path, for example, can be a metaphor for thinking about arithmetic. The path starts at some point 0 and as children walk along, every step takes them 1 unit further from the starting point; they can even take half steps or skip along two steps at a time. If they want to imagine what it might mean to add 5 and 9, they could think of first walking 9 steps and then walking 5 more. But that also helps them think about what $14 - 3$ might mean because they can imagine walking backwards. They might be sitting still as they imagine all of this walking back and forth along their path; but they are reliving, at least in their imagination, the movement of their feet. If they close their eyes, they might even imagine the shape of the path, the smell of the trees, the sound that is made when they step on the dried leaves.

Once they have imagined this environment, with a path and motion forward or backward along it, they might find the environment talking back at them, suggesting new actions they could take. What if they kept on walking forever? What if they turned around and walked back towards the starting point: what kind of operation might that be? What if they walked back *past* the starting point? What if they came to an intersection and followed the path perpendicular to the one they had been on? These are exactly the kinds of actions that mathematicians make. In order to help them see and explore, sometimes they imagine the actions and sometimes they draw them out.

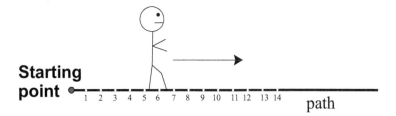

There's still something quite abstract to this environment, as we've taken out many features that would normally be part of it. In the drawing, the path is just a line and it comes labelled with numbers, which is rarely the case when you go for a walk! But instead of thinking of this environment as abstract, we could say it overemphasises the number of steps, the direction of the walking and its relation to the starting point, while underemphasising details of the surroundings, such as where the path is and whether it's paved. In other words, we're underemphasising the things that people normally care about when they think of going for a walk along a path. We think that when people say 'Maths is hard because it's abstract' they're alluding, at least in part, to the way that maths doesn't care about the things they care about. From this, they deduce that maths doesn't care about anything. But it does – it just cares in a different way, a way that's often not made very clear to learners.

Caring mathematics

A common approach to helping students develop connections to maths is to come up with problems that link to everyday experiences, such as tasks about sports teams or mobile phone plans or even problems involving celebrities. In fact, such problems have been a staple of maths textbooks for hundreds of years; indeed, in some cases, they have been the main approach used. But many 'real life' problems are so artificial that they don't do much to help children make connections (either between themselves and the problem, or between themselves and the maths involved).

For example, as many young children love animals, problems such as the following are often seen as engaging: 'There are 19 cows and some chickens at the farm. Together, there are 74 legs. How many chickens are there?' This problem is artificial because there's no reason for someone on a farm to add the number of legs of cows and chickens together. Why would you add the legs instead of simply counting the chickens? Despite the intention to make the problem about familiar, concrete things, the problem is probably quite abstract to many pupils, as it doesn't relate to their life experiences – how many children have ever been on a farm? The farm situation is just a ploy to get pupils to do arithmetic, i.e. 'We're going to talk about things you love, but we're going to do so in a way that doesn't relate to why you care about them.'

There are situations in which the total number of a given attribute might matter. A farmer, for example, might care about the number of tyres needed for all of the farm equipment in order to do an order. Perhaps the problem could be rescued with enough context, but it's unlikely to get at something that both mathematics and pupils might care about. And this might be getting close to the main issue with maths teaching and learning. Not how to make it fun or easy (or concrete!), but how to align what maths cares about and what learners care about. We recognise that the phrase 'What maths cares about' is unusual grammar, but we're using it deliberately. We're inviting you to consider maths as an entity in its own right, an entity with personality and even desires. In short, we're inviting you to consider mathematics as something you, or pupils, might come into a relationship with. A relationship in which you're open to being changed, as maths itself is open to changing. Anyone's free to choose new sets of assumptions, to define new rules, new geometries, new algebras, new numbers, and to explore what the mathematical implications are. But once those assumptions are chosen, maths cares about them being applied consistently and about the full range of those implications being explored.

To close this chapter, and not leave the farm stranded, let's have a look at the original problem to see what maths might care about. This problem invites students into working with unknown quantities (in this case, the number of chickens) by using all the available information (in this case, not only the numbers 19 and 74, but the fact that cows have 4 legs and chickens have 2). There are just enough known quantities here in order to figure out the unknown one. It's actually like a

Sudoku puzzle, when you have enough information to figure out what number goes in an empty square. Indeed, games and puzzles are terrific ways of engaging pupils in solving unknowns. Many people love doing puzzles, which means they can provide pupils with a sense of connection. Puzzles are playful, but they also usually involve repetition, which helps build fluency. For example, Kenken puzzles involve exactly the same kind of operations as the farm problem (products, sums and differences). But they offer that sense of satisfaction that mathematicians find so rewarding, which is not often the case with word problems in maths class.

Another game that helps pupils feel a connection is 'guess my number', which can be done with the same kind of operations used to solve the farm problem. Pupils are asked to think of a number, any number, to perform a sequence of operations on that number, and finally to predict what the result will be. It could go like this:

1. Start with a number.

2. Double the number.

3. Add 4.

4. Divide by 2.

5. Subtract the number you started with.

6. Your answer is 2!

Starting with their own number gives children a sense of ownership and perhaps even individuality – they could have chosen 1 or 574 or $\frac{17}{8}$ or -5. The choice that is given is not just meant to make them feel special; it is part of the mathematics – it matters that they could start with *any* number. And with all of the things that they were asked to do with their number, it certainly does not seem like the operation was straightforward. There is a sense of mystery here: how did we know that their answer would be 2? How is that possible? How would it be possible if everyone who reads this book chooses a different answer?

Another way of forging a connection might be to use objects in the classroom with which pupils already have experiences. Cuisenaire rods, for example, can be used to create a farm-like situation. 'If there are 19 purple rods placed in a long line, head to toe, then how many red rods would be needed to make the line be the same length as 74 white rods?'

As you can see, the quantities are the same, but the context would be more relational. It is also quite empirical, since some pupils might begin by actually creating the long line of rods. Since maths cares less about specific examples and more about general relationships, this particular configuration could be just a starting point. What if we actually use 20 purple rods? Could light green rods be used instead of red ones? This is like bringing a three-legged creature into the farm scenario!

Putting into practice E: Learning number

Children's earliest experiences with number language usually involve reciting the number sequence, 'One, two, three, four, ...' It's part of many childhood songs and games. When children begin formal schooling, they're invited to use these words to help them count objects. They are often given blocks or counters or other objects to manipulate and point to. Later on, they're asked to count objects drawn in books and on worksheets. Eventually they learn how to write and read the symbols associated with these numbers – the Hindu-Arabic numerals 1, 2, 3, 4, and so on. These steps progress as follows:

- enactive – manipulating objects
- iconic – using visual representations
- symbolic – working with signs, such as numerals

It seems like quite a natural progression. It seems so natural that it's often assumed that manipulating objects is easier and more concrete, while working with symbols is harder or more abstract – and should therefore be reserved for older children. We've heard many primary school teachers shy away from introducing students to symbols at an early age, for fear of putting them off or robbing them of the chance to get a tangible 'feel' for quantity.

This is a valid concern. Valerie Walkerdine's research (mentioned in Dogma C) highlighted the way in which children experience mathematical signs as arbitrary and meaningless, and imposed from the top down by the teacher as an authority figure. In these cases, mathematical symbols can seem devoid of humanness – they have no colour, warmth, nuance or tangibility.

But if symbols are encountered in the context of relationships or connections, this makes them more accessible. And in terms of learning number, since the development of symbolic fluency has been shown to predict students' success in maths (Lyons & Beilock, 2013), it's important for children to have many opportunities, even early on, to engage meaningfully with symbols. There are many ways of doing so, including the approach that was discussed in Putting into practice A using Cuisenaire rods. In this chapter, we'll share a method that uses digital technologies, which can be particularly powerful for bringing together the physical worlds of manipulation with the digital world of dynamic images and symbols.

Extending the power of fingers

When we point to objects in the environment, like chairs and books, they're quite passive while being counted. In contrast, when children touch the iPad screen with their fingers in *TouchCounts*, they create an object (a coloured disc). This object announces its own number name, e.g. 'one' as well as being labelled with the associated symbol (1). *TouchCounts* is a free iPad application, which you could try out for yourself, or get a sense of by watching some videos (go to YouTube and search on *TouchCounts* – as a single word). In this section, we will be describing some of the things we've learned about children's understanding of number while working with *TouchCounts*, much of which we think can be useful even if you don't have access to the application.

With *TouchCounts*, a child can use their index finger to tap on the screen four times, one after another. The child hears 'one, two, three, four' and sees four discs, one after the other. On each of these discs, a number symbol appears: 1, 2, 3, 4. In other words, the child engages with enactive (touching the screen), iconic (seeing a visual representation of one then two then three then four objects) and symbolic methods simultaneously.

It's important that the symbols on the discs accompany and extend these experiences, rather than being extracted from the tangible visual and aural experience. This is probably why so many children express delight around the symbols, especially when they reach numbers like 100 or even higher. They've seen these numbers before, in games, at the supermarket, in books, but they've never *made* them. Making big numbers is exciting: it feels sophisticated and it extends the power of the fingers to well beyond 10. The possibility of being able to tap one more time, no matter whether you've got to 5, to 10, to 100, seeds the idea of infinity. You can keep tapping and tapping, and each time a new number name will be said and a new symbol will appear, with no end in sight.

It's the act of using fingers that makes these experiences so significant for learners. Research has shown that fingers are extremely important in the development of number sense. Not only do learners need to be able to differentiate between their fingers in order to learn number, but they need to use their fingers to count with (through pointing) and count on (for calculating). There's a neurofunctional link between the finger and the calculating areas of the brain. Using *TouchCounts* can help children develop their finger gnosis, which literally means 'finger knowing'. They physically learn to use their fingers to create one or more discs at a time, but also develop powerful ways of thinking and communicating about number.

For example, in the picture below, a young girl has been asked to 'make four all-at-once' which means she needs to put four fingers down simultaneously. As she practises doing this, perhaps initially only placing only two fingers down and then five, she eventually develops motor fluency in making a four-fingered gesture. When she lifts her fingers off the screen, she can use this gesture to explain to another classmate what she's made. She can also use this gesture to compute a sum, such as 4 + 3, by adding on. Through *TouchCounts*, the girl has turned her own fingers into even better allies. (This links to our discussion, in Dogma D, about how we help individual learners by focusing on creating situations in which they can act successfully, as well as giving them the tools and resources to do so.)

Where are the meanings?

A grade-one (Year 2 equivalent) classroom teacher named Eileen Bennison working in British Columbia helped us to understand the different kinds of meanings pupils can develop about number. Eileen projected the screen of a tablet onto a whiteboard, and let the children take turns pressing the screen with their fingers. After counting up to 10, one child suggested they go all the way to 100. The children were surprised by how long this took. After all the anticipation – and they didn't even seem to know when exactly 100 would come – there was a big outburst of cheering once the words 'one hundred' were finally heard.

When recounting this story during a presentation at a practitioner conference, another teacher expressed concern that the experience wasn't physical or concrete enough, which led to the following conversation:

Teacher: The kids need to be able to see what a hundred really is.

Nathalie: They can get a different sense of a hundred by seeing how long it takes to get to a hundred by counting though.

Teacher: Yes, but that doesn't help them estimate what a hundred really looks like, like when you have to solve a problem involving a hundred things.

Nathalie: Yes, for estimation, I can see why you say that. But I think there are other situations in which you might not need to know what a hundred really looks like. Imagine, for example, you were asked what comes after a hundred and twenty-four.

Teacher: But the kids need to be able to know that a hundred and twenty-four is one hundred and twenty and four.

We agree with the teacher that there's value in having a cardinal understanding of 100 and having experiences seeing, and even manipulating, one hundred objects, like when using Dienes blocks or Cuisenaire rods. In associating the meaning of one hundred with 'what one hundred looks like', the focus is on a physical, concrete or iconic representation of the quantity one hundred. However, when pupils count up to one hundred in *TouchCounts*, they experience a temporal and symbolic sense of one hundred, as well as the one hundred discs on the screen. One hundred is not only a lot, but it takes a long time to get there.

Indeed, Eileen told us that after getting to one hundred, the children were eager to keep going. After a few more touches were added, a boy exclaimed 'Oh! It's not two hundred.'

Eileen:	What did you say?
Boy:	It's not two hundred.
Eileen:	Why do you say that?
Boy:	I thought that two hundred was right after one hundred, but it's not.
Eileen:	No, how far away is it from one hundred?
Boy:	It's, it's, it's one more hundred away from one hundred.

This exchange is remarkable because it shows both what the boy thought would happen after one hundred, which according to the research is quite common, and also how he makes sense of 200 in relation to 100 through a temporal, and perhaps even symbolic way, rather than through a visual representation.

The boy's thinking about number and about place value draws on knowledge built up through multiple foundations and not just one, similar to the image of the mangrove forest used in Dogma A. There are, of course, other parts of his knowledge that might be helpful and relevant later on, which might offer different ways of thinking about the relation between 100 and 200.

Feeding back into thinking

Some of the negative experiences that learners have with maths are related to the kind of authority that teachers and textbooks hold. This is especially true when teachers and textbooks are the sources of all of the answers, as well as all of the questions deemed worth asking. Changing the feedback loop can provide learners with a good sense of agency – a feeling that they can act on their own accord, without having to wait for the teacher. For example, what if something in the environment can provide feedback on whether a learner has done something correctly or come up with a good answer? Imagine you're trying to open a combination lock. You try a code you think might work. But you don't have to wait to ask anyone else if you're right or not; you can just tug at the lock to see if it opens.

If it doesn't, nobody else needs to know you were wrong and you can just try another one.

This kind of situation – where the environment provides feedback, rather than an authority figure – is quite common outside of the classroom. But it can happen in the classroom as well. Many scholars have shown how digital technologies can provide rich feedback, not just about whether pupils have done something right or wrong, but sometimes also how they can do it better.

For example, sticking with the example of *TouchCounts*, we often use a task with children aged five or six that uses the gravity setting, in which numbers created on the screen fall down off the screen unless they're placed on a 'shelf' (a horizontal line) near the top of the screen. The task is: place just 5 on the shelf. These children know how to count, in the sense that they can say 'one, two, three, four, five, six…' often going up to ten or even further. So they assume this will be an easy task. They might begin by tapping above the shelf, in which case they get something like in the image below. In such cases, the teacher can remind them that the task is to put *just* five on the shelf. Then, typically, they start tapping below the shelf multiple times, until they hear the word 'five'. At this point, they know that they haven't put five on the shelf, and they don't need the teacher to tell them so.

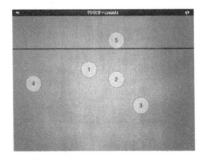

The environment provides the necessary feedback. On their second try, children often slow down their tapping and start listening to what's being said, but frequently still place five below the shelf. However, it's likely they've also heard what came before five. The environment isn't just providing an assessment of whether or not the task has been done correctly, but also some feedback on how it can be done successfully in future attempts. So, on their third try, after hearing 'four' they might pause and move their finger up to touch above the shelf. If they do so, they'll hear 'five' and see the disc labelled with a 5 sitting on the shelf, so they'll know they've succeeded. They'll show their satisfaction and pride as well, which is caused by solving the task rather than by pleasing the teacher.

For older learners, the task can be varied by asking for larger numbers, or working in the 13–19 range, which causes many difficulties for young learners, or perhaps using double digits as a way of working on place value, or even a sequence like 3, 6, 9, 12 to engage in skip counting. Whatever the case, the important point is that the learning environment creates a strong feedback loop that no longer requires an external source of judgement. It's in using this feedback loop that meanings and connections are made.

Motion and memory

An important feature of the perceived abstractness of maths and its lack of humanness, is its lack of motion. Humans are constantly moving, even in our sleep. We pay attention to our own movements and others' – how they walk or lift their eyebrows, whether they are coming too close or trying to sneak by. Humans are all about behaviour. Maths, on the other hand, is often seen or presented as static: symbols don't move; numbers don't go anywhere; shapes don't walk or run or hug. And in the classroom, we sometimes ask pupils to imitate maths by sitting still at their desks and moving only the invisible neurons in the brain.

With insights from recent theories of embodied cognition, we're starting to understand that movement is a crucial part of learning. We discussed in Dogma E how basic concepts in arithmetic can be understood through metaphors – the idea of addition relates to the act of gathering two groups of objects into one, or to walking along a path by a certain distance in order to get to an endpoint. These insights can help us to find ways to support learning better, for example, by inviting children to actually walk along a path and associate that walking with a distance. This example comes from basic arithmetic, but if we accept the idea of embodied cognition, then even concepts found in secondary school and in research mathematics could be linked to powerful sensorimotor experiences!

These insights helped to inform the design of *TouchCounts*, particularly in relation to adding and subtracting. We've been discussing examples from the 'counting world' in *TouchCounts* so far, however, there's a second world in the app called the 'operations world', where the main form of interaction is through contact gestures. These gestures invite pupils to use certain movements associated with mathematical concepts. Let's look at this more closely.

If you place four fingers down all at once in the operation world, you make one large disc that contains four smaller coloured discs as well as the label 4, and the aural number name 'four'. We call this a 'herd' of four, to describe four in its cardinal form: as one object that represents many. If you also make a herd of ten, you have two herds on the screen. If you place your thumb on one herd and your index finger on the other, and pinch your thumb and finger together, the herds will overlap and become one. That herd is labelled 14 and 'fourteen' will be said aloud. The history of that 14 is preserved through colour, since four of the smaller discs are one colour and ten another.

The pinching gesture makes a static symbol, the arithmetic sign for addition +, a temporal, motor action. But it's not just any action – it's an action that expresses the idea of addition as gathering two groups of objects together. Once pupils have tried creating herds and pinching them together, the teacher can then ask them to write down an equation that corresponds to what they've done in the app, e.g. children might write 4 + 10 = 14 for the example above.

The idea isn't to get rid of static signs but to associate them with actions. In this case, the actions are gestures. The advantage of gestures is that they're not only for pinching objects on the screen, but they can be used to communicate with others as well, for example, if a child makes a pinching gesture in the air to explain how they produced a herd of eight. Gestures are helpful for manipulating and communicating, but they are also important for remembering. We have aural and visual memory, but we also have kinesthetic memory. If a child is asked to figure out the sum of two numbers, they might call upon this kinesthetic memory to re-enact a pinching gesture they remember.

Pupils can also perform subtraction, the inverse of addition, on *TouchCounts* using the opposite of the pinching gesture. To subtract, you put your thumb and index finger on a herd and then separate them in order to 'take out' a smaller herd. The further you separate them, the larger the herd taken out. It's possible to add or subtract multiple herds simultaneously by using multiple fingers. If all of the herds are the same size, this multi-pinching gesture can provide a strong sensorimotor experience of multiplication or division.

In all of these examples, it's difficult to draw the line between concrete and abstract, since the creation and manipulation of mathematical objects and symbols is about concrete *and* abstract. Many of the binaries that feature in school maths seem to dissolve as well, since children are engaged in procedural *and* conceptual thinking; in physical *and* mental activity; in memorising *and* reasoning; in feeling *and* thinking.

Summary

In Dogma E and this chapter, we worked through the idea that 'Maths is hard because it is abstract'. Some of the ideas around this dogma came from early developmental theories that presumed that children should always begin with concrete, physical objects in their learning of maths. We suggested that a relational view in which the attributes 'concrete' and 'abstract' describe connections instead of things could open up the possibility of early experiences with symbols, for example. We showed what this might look like in the *TouchCounts* environment, where children not only work with symbols right from the start – at three years old – but are also encouraged to explore large numbers, often considered beyond the scope of their capacities. This reminds us of Dave Hewitt's (1996) idea of subordination, probably best explained by this: 'If you want to practise walking then start learning to run' (p. 28). As children run through the 30s, 60s, 120s, etc., which are exciting numbers that they are only beginning to touch, they have to pass through 1–10 and 11–20; they're hearing the 'three' in 'forty-three' etc. and seeing the symbols 7, 8, 9, 0 appear over and over again.

We feel that this sense of excitement and even wonder is crucial to developing connections with maths; that it needs to include emotion as well as just being something intellectual or cognitive. Our discussion of story in Dogma E tried to evoke the full experience of maths: not only understanding why and figuring out how, but also feeling the wonder and anticipation and surprise and tension that we experience in life. The soap opera idea seems to be a good way to encourage pupils to think of mathematical objects, like numbers and shapes, as being worth knowing about and capable of adventures and romances. A lovely example of how one primary school teacher mobilises the idea of mathematical objects as characters is by treating each day of the month as a focus of investigation. For example, 'Today, it's 7th October. What do we know about 7?' This is a 'mangrove forest' type question – it invites new thinking about 7 that doesn't depend on a single, central idea. Pupils might get to a particular understanding that the teacher has in mind, like the idea that 7 comes after 6 on the calendar. But they might get to other understandings as well – that under 7, we find 14; that there are three 7s on the calendar for the month of October; that 7 is also the number of days in a week. It's all these connections that give 7 its 'personality', that make 7 worth getting to know. Some connections will be very powerful for some students and others for other students.

Epilogue

Given some of the difficulties that can be caused by learning maths, it's a fair question to ask whether it's worth it. One response to 'I can't do maths' is to say, 'Well, that doesn't actually matter.' We firmly believe that being able to do maths *does* matter and, as we've shown, there's no reason why every child who speaks a language can't be successful at primary maths. Societies across the globe are becoming ever more technological. Statistics are everywhere, and used to justify actions and inactions. Models of climate, virus spread, extreme weather, to name just a few, are becoming an increasing part of mainstream media in many countries. In such contexts, it seems to us more important than ever that citizens are able to understand and interrogate the maths presented to them. For anyone who uses a smartphone, algorithms increasingly influence personal decisions (such as which route to take on a journey or what to buy) and personal data is stored and sold, often with little oversight. Again, being comfortable with maths seems necessary for engaging in the implications of algorithms and the uses made of our own data.

But we also believe there's something worthwhile in the study of maths for its own sake. Much like literature or art, maths can be appreciated. Almost all children we meet seem fascinated by ideas of infinity, and maths almost always touches on ideas of infinity. Any pattern pupils notice begs the question of whether it continues – and that is a question that reaches out to infinity. Learning maths can also provide opportunities for learning about yourself and for experiencing significant desires of human flourishing, as Francis Su (2020) argues – including play, beauty, truth, struggle, power, justice, community and even love! We hope we've offered some small insights into these aspects of the subject, through giving classroom examples and tasks.

In each of the chapters introducing a dogma, we showed contrasting images, hoping it would help to consider both together. We end this book by bringing the five sets of images together. We hope that they help to make the dogmas clear, and act as a reminder that there are alternative perspectives, alternative ways of being and knowing. The mathematics educator David Wheeler said that he did not want all children to become mathematicians, but he did want them to have at least one experience of 'mathematising', so they knew what they were turning away from (2001). We feel the same way.

A child who says 'I can't do maths!' is unlikely to want or have such an experience of 'mathematising'; it's likely they're caught in the web of the five dogmas. A maths classroom in which many pupils feel like this probably embodies several of the dogmas we have discussed, such as the arrow thinking of 'Maths is hard because it is abstract' and the binary assumption of 'Maths is always right or wrong' and the tree metaphor of 'Maths is a building block subject'.

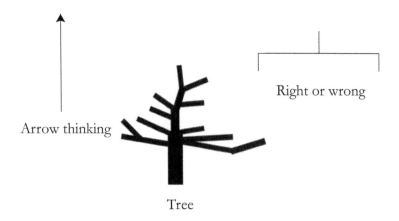

Arrow thinking

Right or wrong

Tree

Expanding the dogmas, perhaps by engaging children in the algebra task with Cuisenaire rods described in Putting into practice A, can change the feeling of the classroom, moving more towards a 'mangrove forest'. Doing so helps children see that there are different ways of understanding ideas, ways that might involve touching objects and reasoning with colour.

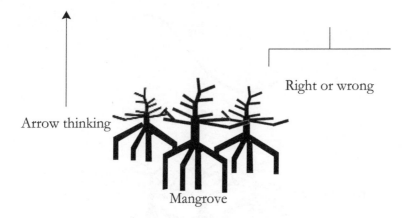

Arrow thinking

Right or wrong

Mangrove

In our experience, once this letting go of one dogma begins, there's a ripple effect across others. So, as you work with the expressions describing the Cuisenaire rods, children begin to see that there can be multiple ways of arriving at and expressing solutions, thus moving away from the right–wrong binary.

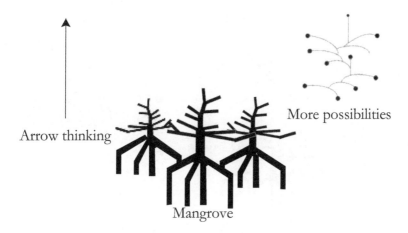

Arrow thinking

More possibilities

Mangrove

Then some of the children in your class who didn't used to shine start to find their voices, and the class begins to realise that being good at maths might depend on the problem being worked on or the tools available to work with.

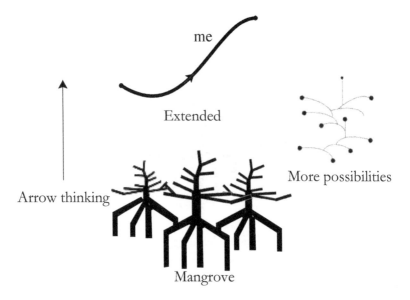

Maybe after this activity, it's time to prepare report cards, and parents will expect to have a very clear picture of their children's achievement, which might make more visible the 'Maths is culture-free' dogma.

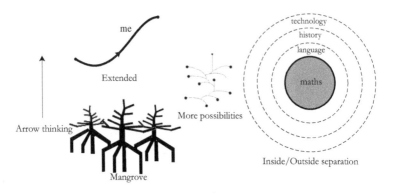

As you can see, there are many combinations and possibilities, and they will change according to the particular opportunities and constraints you have, which might include the time of the year, the topic, the classroom dynamics and so on. Our aim in showing these possibilities is to stress, once again, that there are not just two ways of doing things. There are many assumptions made in the maths classroom and it's possible to take small-scale actions which may only affect one or two dogmas, but which will go a long way in helping more learners to feel that they can do maths.

References

Abdulrahim, N., & Orosco, M. (2020). 'Culturally responsive mathematics teaching: A research synthesis', *Urban Review*, **52**, 1–25.

Ainsworth, C. (2016). 'Consistency of imagery', *Mathematics Teaching*, **253**, 15–19.

Averill, R., Anderson, D., Easton, H., Te Maro, P., Smith, D., & Hynds, A. (2009). 'Culturally responsive teaching of mathematics: Three models from linked studies', *Journal for Research in Mathematics Education*, **40**(2), 157–186.

Banwell, C. S. Saunders, K. D. and Tahta, D. S. (1972). *Starting Points*. Oxford: Oxford University Press.

Bishop, A.J. (1988). *Mathematical Enculturation: A Cultural Perspective on Mathematics Education*. Kluwer Academic Publishers: Amsterdam.

Brown, S., & Walter, M. (2005). *The Art of Problem Posing*. 3rd edn. Oxford: Routledge.

Bronx Charter Schools for Better Learning. (2019). *Annual Reports*. Available at: https://4.files.edl.io/e6b3/11/26/19/184819-d89b0090-5f6a-4424-8b01-63466e74147a.pdf

Buerk, D. (1982). 'An experience with some able women who avoid mathematics', *For the Learning of Mathematics* **3**(2), 19–24.

Bushnell, K. (2018). 'Learning mathematics for an environmentally sustainable future,' *Mathematics Teaching*, **263**, 35–39.

Cockcroft, W. H. (1982). *Mathematics counts*. London: HMSO.

Coles, A. (2015). *Engaging in mathematics in the classroom*. Oxford: Routledge.

Coles, A., Darron, J. & Rolph, B. (2022). 'Communicating climate change information', *Mathematics Teaching*, **280**, 2–7.

Cooperrider, K., & Gentner, D. (2019). 'The career of measurement', *Cognition*, **191**, 1–12.

Curriculum Research & Development Group, University of Hawai'i at Mānoa. (unknown). *Measure Up*. Available at: https://manoa.hawaii.edu/crdg/research-development/research-programs/mathematics/%20measure-up

Devlin, K. (2001). *The Math Gene: How Mathematical Thinking Evolved and Why Numbers are Like Gossip*. London: Basic Books. See also: www.discovermagazine.com/the-sciences/keith-devlinthe-joy-of-math

Dietiker, L. (2012). *The mathematics textbook as story: A literary approach to interrogating mathematics curriculum*. Unpublished PhD dissertation. Michigan State University.

Franke, M., Kazemi, E. & Chan Turrou, A. (2018). *Choral Counting & Counting Collections: Transforming the PreK-5 Math Classroom*. Stenhouse: Portsmouth, US.

Gattegno, C. (1963). *Mathematics with numbers in colour Book 1: Qualitative arithmetic, The study of numbers from 1 to 20*. Educational Explorers Ltd.

Gattegno, C. (1974). *The common sense of teaching mathematics.* New York: Educational Solutions Worldwide Inc. (reprinted 2010).

Gerofsky, S. (1996). 'A linguistic and narrative view of word problems in mathematics education', *For the learning of mathematics*, **16**(2), 36–45.

Gladwell, M. (2008). *Outliers: The story of success.* London: Penguin.

Goutard, M. (1964). *Mathematics and Children: a reappraisal of our attitude.* Educational Explorers Ltd.

Hewitt, D. (1999). 'Arbitrary and necessary part 1: A way of viewing the mathematics curriculum', *For the Learning of Mathematics*, 19(3), pp. 2-9.

Lakatos, I. (1976). *Proofs and refutations: The logic of mathematical discovery.* Cambridge: Cambridge University Press.

Lunney Borden, L. (2011). 'The 'verbification' of mathematics: using the grammatical structures of Mi'kmaq to support student learning', *For the Learning of Mathematics*, **31**(3), 8–13.

Lyons I., Beilock S. (2013). 'Ordinality and the nature of symbolic numbers', *Journal of Neuroscience*, **33**(43):17052–61.

McGuire, J. & Evans, K. (2018). 'Finding a need for measurement: The case of the alien's underpants', *Mathematics Teaching*, **261**, 36–40.

National Film Board of Canada. (1961). *Mathematics At Your Fingertips clip 1 of 3.* Available at: www.youtube.com/watch?v=ae0McT5WYa8

O'Neil, C. (2016). *Weapons of math destruction: How big data increases inequality and threatens democracy.* London: Penguin.

Ormesher, C. (2021). Slow pedagogies. *Mathematics Teaching,* **276**, 22–24.

Papert, S. (1980). *Mindstorms: Children, computers and powerful ideas.* London: Basic Books.

Picker, S. H., & Berry, J. S. (2000). 'Investigating pupils' images of mathematicians', *Educational Studies in Mathematics*, 43(1), 65–94.

Renert, M. (2011). 'Mathematics for life: Sustainable mathematics education', *For the Learning of Mathematics*, **31**(1), 20–26.

Su, F. (2020). *Mathematics for human flourishing.* New Haven: Yale University Press.

Walkerdine, V. (1990). 'Difference, cognition and mathematics education', *For the Learning of Mathematics*, **10**(3), 51–56.

Watson, A. (2021). *Care in mathematics education: Alternative educational spaces and practices.* London: Palgrave Macmillan.

Wheeler, D. (2001). 'Mathematisation as a Pedagogical Tool', *For the Learning of Mathematics*, 21(2), 50–53. http://www.jstor.org/stable/40248362

Wilensky, U. (1991). 'Abstract meditations on the concrete and concrete implications for mathematics education', in I. Harel & S. Papert (eds.). *Constructionism.* New York: Ablex Publishing Corporation, pp. 193–204.

Zalasiewicz, J. (2010). *The planet in a pebble: A journey into Earth's deep history.* Oxford: Oxford University Press.

Index